# CITIES OF HUNGER

## urban malnutrition in developing countries

Clive Offley/OXFAM

C000022161

# JANE PRYER AND NIGEL CROOK

First published 1988
© Oxfam 1988
Revised edition October 1990
© Oxfam 1990

Jane Pryer,
Centre for Human Nutrition,
University of Sheffield,
and
Nigel Crook,
Department of Economic and Political Studies,
School of Oriental and African Studies,
University of London.


**British Library Cataloguing in Publication Data**

Pryer, Jane
    Cities of hunger : urban malnutrition in
    developing countries.
    1.   Developing countries. Man. Malnutrition. Relief
    I.   Title
    II.   Crook, Nigel
    363.8'5

ISBN 085598 154 7 Hardback
        085598 155 5 Paperback


Printed by
Oxfam Print Unit

Published by
Oxfam,
274 Banbury Road,
Oxford, OX2 7DZ,
United Kingdom.

# CONTENTS

**Preface**

**Part One: Malnutrition in the City — Tools for Analysis**

# Part Two: Case Studies of Urban Nutrition Intervention Projects

# ACKNOWLEDGEMENTS

We should like to acknowledge gratefully the help we received from Trish Silkin and Osvaldo Vasquez of the Catholic Institute of International Relations, from Mike Bailey of Christian Aid, and from Bridget Wooding of Oxfam, who gave us access to excellent documentation on the case studies; from Jenny Amery, Roberto Lopez, Maria Colemont and Leslie Roberts who made valuable observations on the case studies from their own knowledge of the projects in question. We should also like to thank those from whom we received similar help but who would rather remain unmentioned.

Sincere thanks are due to Meera Bapat, Edward Clay, Liz Dowler, Stuart Gillespie, Barbara Harriss, Wendy McLean, David Nabarro, Gabrielle Palmer, Sue Rifkin, John Rivers, Patti Rundall and Erica Wheeler, who all gave extremely helpful and constructive comments on the text. We are most grateful for editorial guidance from Trudy Harpham and Tim Lusty of the Oxfam Health Unit, and from Julia Schiff in Oxfam's Publications Department. Translations from Spanish were efficiently undertaken by Ena Aracil. Finally, Jane Pryer would like to thank Ulrich Freudenstein for encouragement and support throughout the preparation of this book.

We are sincerely grateful to all for the time and patience they offered us. Responsibility, however, for the views (and any errors) that have emerged lies fairly and squarely with the authors.

Jane Pryer
Nigel Crook

July, 1987

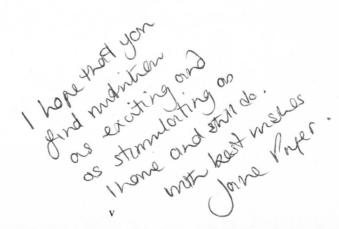

# PREFACE

In 1985 Oxfam, UNICEF and the London School of Hygiene and Tropical Medicine organised a workshop, held in Oxford, on the question of urban health care in developing countries. Two publications have resulted from this meeting: one is a book edited by Trudy Harpham, Tim Lusty and Patrick Vaughan entitled *In the Shadow of the City: health and the urban poor in developing countries*; and the other is this booklet on urban malnutrition.

We appreciate that much of what can be said about **urban** malnutrition could equally be said of **rural** malnutrition. Basic underlying causes – such as severe poverty, a deleterious environment, and unequal social and economic relations – are common to both rural and urban malnutrition. But these causes have different effects in urban and rural areas; this booklet is about their urban effects, and is therefore more specifically addressed to people interested or working in urban areas in the field of nutrition. Some of these specifically urban effects are summarised in Chapter 1.

The booklet is divided into two parts. The first part presents recent views on the measurement and consequences of malnutrition. It then suggests a framework for analysing the causes of malnutrition in the urban context. Overall, the first part offers tools for use in the analytical understanding of malnutrition in a city.

The second part documents in some detail three factual case studies of nutrition intervention projects in predominantly urban localities: one in the Caribbean, one in Latin America, and one in Asia. It makes use of some of the tools of analysis introduced in the first part, and describes the possibilities and problems encountered in the practical application of a broad approach to nutritional intervention. We hope that the projects discussed will be an inspiration, for they illustrate what can be done to improve the lives of some of the poorest people in the world.

This book has been used by undergraduate and postgraduate students in the fields of health, population and development, as well as by project staff and the organisers of training programmes in the field of urban health in developing countries. It should also be of interest to a more general readership in the development field. This reprint includes a new section on the effects of structural adjustment policies on the urban poor.

# PART ONE : MALNUTRITION IN THE CITY–
## tools for analysis

# CHAPTER 1.

## URBANISATION AND ITS CONSEQUENCES FOR HEALTH AND NUTRITION

### 1.1. The facts of urbanisation

Until recently, it was often thought that concern for the urban populations of the less developed countries was unjustified: their populations were largely rural, and urban areas were economically privileged and hence presumably their people were relatively healthy and well fed. As recently as 1975 only 28% of the world's population was urban. But by the year 2000, this will have risen to about one-half; and by 2025 to about two-thirds. **In fact in 15 years from now the rural population living in the less developed world will begin to decrease, while the urban populations keep on growing.**

### 1.2. Why are the rates of urbanisation so high?

Contrary to popular opinion, migration is no longer the principal cause of this urban growth. A study [1] of the United Nations Population Division has shown that, overall, natural increase in urban areas is now responsible for an average of 61% of the urban population growth in developing countries, as compared with only 39% through rural-urban migration.

While the developing countries are in general experiencing urbanisation at an unprecedented rate, there are obviously regional differences. In regions where the level of urbanisation is already particularly high – as in Latin America – a large proportion of the urban population growth is likely to be due to a natural increase in urban areas rather than to rural-urban migration. By way of contrast, regions which have lower absolute levels of urbanisation – such as Sub-Saharan Africa and parts of Asia – are experiencing high levels of rural-urban migration and a rapid rate of urban growth. This is particularly important because **it is not only the absolute level of urbanisation that has detrimental consequences on the health, economic and social development of**

---

[1] Rossi-Espagnet, 'Primary health care in urban areas: reaching the urban poor in developing countries.' A State of the Art report. *UNICEF/WHO Report No SHS/84.4*, 1984. World Health Organisation, Geneva, Switzerland.

**the urban population, but also the relative speed of change** causing increased demands for facilities, services and resources that frequently outstrip the ability of governments to supply them.

It is commonly believed that the urbanisation process occurring in developing countries is similar to the experience of the Western capitalist countries in the nineteenth century. As a result of a rapid increase in the growth of manufacturing industry (with its attendant administrative and commercial facilities) the need arose for large local concentrations of the work force. The consequent migration of labour from rural areas led to the formation of urban populations, and a rise in the proportion of the population living in cities to the levels that prevail in the West today.

In many cases, however, the application of this economic model of urbanisation to the situation in developing countries today is questionable, because urbanisation has often occurred independently of any surge in prosperity through large-scale industrialisation. Hence, the level of urbanisation (i.e. the percentage of urban to total population) and the rate of urban expansion (i.e. the percentage increase in the urban population), may not always be caused by the 'pull' of economic prosperity and opportunity in the cities; **it is sometimes caused by the 'push' from the rural areas due to significant changes in the mode of production in agriculture, and to the increased concentration of the ownership of land in the hands of the few, which have led to a situation in which there is a steady increase in the proportion of the rural population who are compelled to seek a living outside agriculture.**

Disruptive events such as drought, earthquakes, storms, floods, guerilla warfare and civil war have also contributed to a further push of rural-urban migration in many developing countries.

## 1.3. What are the consequences of this rate of urban growth?

Many problems have been associated with the rapid rate of urban expansion. Some are examined below, with their implications for nutrition.

i.      **There has been a rapid increase in the proportion of the urban population living in the appalling conditions of the slums, shanty towns and squatter settlements of cities in developing countries.** In some cities the proportion of the urban population living in such conditions has been estimated to be around 30%, and in other cities estimates are much higher (see Table 1). Even these high estimates are likely to be understatements because of the difficulties of counting the urban poor, and the fact that those in political control often prefer not to recognise or register their existence.

There are many factors which have severe repercussions on the mental and physical health of the people living in the slums and shanty towns of the developing countries: the high population densities, poor makeshift housing, inadequate or non-existent facilities for sanitation and clean water, and environmental as well as industrial pollution; and, because of insecurity of tenure, slum dwellers have little incentive to initiate improvements in their physical environment. Such conditions interact with and contribute to malnutrition amongst slum dwellers.

2

ii.  **The second major problem concerns employment and poverty.**
Many people come to the cities in search of work, and yet in the urban
slums and shanty towns it is usually only a small proportion of the
population who manage to find permanent secure employment in the
modern or formal sector. The majority eke out a living where and when
they can in the so-called 'informal sector' as casual labourers (on
construction sites, in factories, or as coolies), in retail distribution (as
petty traders of food and other commodities), in transport (as rickshaw
and hand-cart pullers or porters), in personal services (shoe shining,
shoe repair, watch and radio repair, tailoring, etc.), in the security
services (as car park attendants or night watchmen) or by begging,
prostitution or theft. Employment for the poorest is often unstable and
insecure, and income is low and unreliable. Again the repercussions on
health and nutrition are likely to be severe.

**Table 1: The proportion of urban populations living in slums around 1980**

| Region and city | City population [in thousands] | % of city population who are slum dwellers/squatters |
|---|---|---|
| **AFRICA** | | |
| Addis Ababa | 1465 | 79 |
| Nairobi | 1162 | 40 |
| Dakar | 799 | 50 |
| Maputo | 384 | 80 |
| **LATIN AMERICA** | | |
| Sao Paolo | 10099 | 55 |
| Lima | 4601 | 40 |
| Santiago | 4100 | 25 |
| **SOUTH ASIA** | | |
| Bombay | 8243 | 45 |
| Calcutta | 9194 | 33 |
| Dhaka | 3459 | 46 |
| Karachi | 5181 | 33 |
| **EAST ASIA** | | |
| Bangkok | 4697 | 23 |
| Jakarta | 6503 | 29 |
| Kuala Lumpur | 920 | 25 |

**Note:** the definition of slum dwellers and squatters differs from country to country.
**Source:** WHO/UNEP, *Urbanization and its implications for child health,* WHO,
Geneva, 1988; K.C. Sivaramakrishnan and L. Green, *Metropolitan
Management: the Asian experience,* Oxford University Press, 1986; *United
Nations, 1986 Demographic Yearbook,* United Nations, New York, 1988.

iii. It is often assumed that entry into the informal sector is easy because qualification barriers are low. However, it is clear from studies conducted in Latin America and Asia that equal access to all by no means always applies. Rather, **as pressure on scarce resources steadily becomes greater, jobs even in the informal sector become heavily controlled by employers.** For example, ease of obtaining a job may be influenced by membership of region of origin, ethnic group, caste, religious community, tribal unit, etc. **In addition, once employment is obtained it is often not a form of independent existence at all, but an outcome of a comprehensive dependency relationship with an employer who is also a social superior.** Employees may claim a minimal livelihood to survive; but often in return they must acknowledge infinite gratitude and accommodation to their employers. Work forms only part of this obligation and has to be supplied when, where and to the degree required by the employer. Ideas of economic mobility and advancement are a mere pipe-dream for the many who are locked into such relationships and are without the necessary capital or education to break the vicious circle of poverty and malnutrition.

iv. **Although the incomes of those working in the informal sector may be higher in money terms than those of landless labourers in the rural areas, this may not imply a higher standard of living.** Most food has to be purchased in the open market and the price may be high. It is true that widespread starvation is unlikely in urban areas since, in a crisis, food usually gets channelled there. Also, public food distribution programmes may operate more efficiently in urban than in rural areas; but the poorest people often do not get easy access to such provisions, as the evidence of persistent malnutrition in urban areas would seem to indicate. In addition, other basic necessities such as fuel, rented accommodation and sometimes even water have to be paid for in urban areas. These costs deplete even further the amount of food that can be bought with the family budget, and all these factors prejudice the nutritional status of the poor.

v. **On migration to urban areas the poor are often confronted with and vulnerable to pressures of modern life with which they are unfamiliar.** Recent migrants may have difficulty finding urban employment as it takes time to build up the necessary contacts to do so. Time is required also to understand and become part of the social networks that will enable the new migrant family to find child-care for its infants if the mother needs to work, or to gain access to medical facilities or food credit systems. Furthermore, at such times of stress new migrants may also be vulnerable to the persuasions of advertising, encouraging the consumption of luxury foods, alcoholic drinks, and baby foods, all of which (directly or indirectly) are likely to have detrimental effects on child nutrition.

4

vi.  Finally, **it should be added that the conditions of work in urban indus-tries may also have harmful implications for health and nutrition.** For instance, women may find employment conflicts with adequate child-care, and especially with breast-feeding. High levels of pollution and dangerous working conditions are often experienced in industrial work-shops, especially in the informal sector. Chronic illness and injury pre-dispose families to malnutrition.

The seriousness of the health and nutritional problem amongst the urban poor may go unnoticed. Data on slum and squatter inhabitants do not always appear in their city's statistics, especially as they are often not officially registered as residents or, if they are included, the reality of their situation is masked by the enormous inequalities in health status that exist between the poor and the middle and upper classes (see Figure 1). The averages that are used as the basis of the city's statistics are therefore very misleading. Appal-ling environmental conditions and intense poverty are likely to be the two most important determinants of health and nutritional status of the slum and shanty town dwellers in many of the cities of the developing countries.

**Figure 1: Infant mortality rates amongst shanty and non-shanty dwellers in Porto Alegre, Brazil.**  *Figures represent deaths per 1000 births*

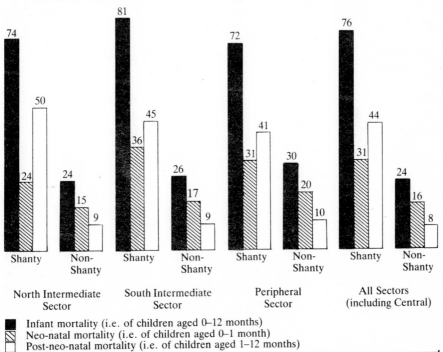

Infant mortality (i.e. of children aged 0–12 months)
Neo-natal mortality (i.e. of children aged 0–1 month)
Post-neo-natal mortality (i.e. of children aged 1–12 months)

Source: J.J. de Lima Guimaraes, A. Fischmann, 'Inequalities in 1980 infant mortality among shanty town residents in the municipality of Porto Alegre, Rio Grande do Sul of Brazil', *PAHO Bulletin* Volume 19:3, pp. 235–251, 1985.

# CHAPTER 2.

# MALNUTRITION – ITS MEASUREMENT AND CONSEQUENCES

It is essential to have a clear understanding of the principal causes and extent of malnutrition in the locality before formulating a policy to reduce and prevent it. This chapter outlines the major types of nutritional deficiency diseases which are prevalent in many urban and rural communities in developing countries and assesses what is known about the consequences of severe malnourishment in young children and adults.

## 2.1. What is malnutrition?

Ideally it should be possible to deduce that people are malnourished if there is evidence that their present or future health status or physical function is impaired due to insufficient supplies of nutrients in their bodies. In practice, however, not all of these relationships have been fully investigated and hence malnutrition tends to be graded according to international conventions. In the context of developing countries the term malnutrition tends to be applied to a wide range of different conditions. These can be briefly summarised as follows:

– Protein Energy Malnutrition: this is a state in which (in its severest form) the physical function of an individual is reduced due to inadequate quantities of food. Functional impairment in this context includes inability to maintain an adequate level of performance for such things as physical growth, resisting and recovering from disease, the states of pregnancy and lactation and physical work.

– Specific nutrient deficiency: this occurs when present or future health status is impaired due to a deficiency of a specific nutrient. For example, nutritional anaemia is usually due to a deficiency of either iron or folate, rickets is due to deficiencies of Vitamin D and/or calcium, and severe deficiencies of Vitamin A can cause blindness.

**It is generally accepted that undernutrition or Protein Energy Malnutrition, resulting from disease and inadequate food energy, is the most widespread**

7

**nutritional problem in developing countries.** Specific nutrient deficiencies – especially Vitamin A deficiency and iron and folate anaemias – are also widely prevalent; however, they frequently occur in conjuction with Protein Energy Malnutrition. In this booklet, therefore, references to malnutrition mean Protein Energy Malnutrition.

## 2.2. How is malnutrition measured in young children?

In practice, children are described as malnourished if their body size or rate of growth is below international growth standards, which are based on 'healthy' American or European children. The technique of measuring body size and growth is called anthropometry. Anthropometric measurements of body size and growth may be taken **regularly** or **intermittently** in order to assess the nutritional status of individuals and communities.

For **regular routine assessments** of the nutritional status of individuals in a community, the most common method is to record the weight of an individual child and to plot it against the child's age on a weight record (sometimes called 'Road to Health Charts' or 'Grow h Charts'). Failure to gain weight, often referred to as faltering, suggests that either the child's diet is inadequate or that he or she is ill, or both.

For **intermittent** assessments of nutritional status, judgements have to be made on the basis of observations and measurements made on **one single occasion.** The measurements most frequently used for this purpose are weight, height or length, and mid-upper arm circumference, which are then compared with international growth standards. A 'nutritional index' is thus obtained, e.g. the percentage of expected weight-for-age, or the percentage of expected weight-for-height. The degree of deficit – i.e. the difference between the measured and the expected value – is used to grade the child's nutritional status.

**The measurement of weight or mid-upper arm circumference in relation to height is used to indicate the degree of thinness or current undernutrition (wasting) that the child may be suffering. The measurement of height or length in relation to age is used to indicate chronic or long-term undernutrition (stunting), which is reflected in retarded bone growth. Whereas the measurement of weight in relation to age used on its own is a composite indicator of both long-term malnutrition (i.e. deficit in height) and current malnutrition (i.e. deficit in weight). It does not distinguish between the two.[2]**

---

[2] For a more detailed discussion on the practical usage of anthropometry the reader is referred to: *Nutrition in Practice – teaching packages on basic and applied nutrition for field workers*,1985. Available from: Dept. of Human Nutrition, London School of Hygiene and Tropical Medicine, Keppel Street, London WC1E 7HT.

## 2.3. What is known about the consequences of malnutrition in young children?

### 2.3.1. Malnutrition and the risk of death

In poor communities in developing countries, between a quarter and a third of the children die before they reach the age of 5 years, and between 10% and 25% may die within the first year of life.

Table 2 illustrates a range of mortality rates during the neonatal period (i.e. the first month of life) and during the first year of life (the infant mortality rate) in both rural and urban locations in the Philippines, India and Brazil.

**Table 2: Infant mortality rates, with rural–urban comparisons.**

| Location | Deaths per 1000 live births | | |
| --- | --- | --- | --- |
| | Total | Neo-natal | Post-neo-natal |
| INDIA (1981) | | | |
| Rural | 120 | 76 | 43 |
| Urban | 63 | 39 | 24 |
| *Bombay (1980–81)* | | | |
| Average | 63 | ★ | ★ |
| Best ward | 46 | ★ | ★ |
| Worst ward | 113 | ★ | ★ |
| PHILIPPINES (1973–77) | | | |
| Rural | 66 | 25 | 41 |
| Urban | 45 | 22 | 23 |
| *Manila (1975)* | | | |
| Average | 76 | 40 | 36 |
| Tondo squatter settlement | 210 | 105 | 105 |
| BRAZIL (1982) | | | |
| Average | 56 | 24 | 32 |
| *Porto Alegre (1982)* | | | |
| Non-shanty areas | 24 | 16 | 8 |
| Shanty areas | 75 | 31 | 44 |

Note: figures not available to the authors indicated ★
Sources: For countries:
India – *Sample Registration Bulletin,* June 1985, Registrar General's Office, New Delhi.
Philippines – *Fertility in the Philippines* (World Fertility Survey Country Study), International Statistical Institute, Voorburg, Netherlands, 1984.
Brazil – *United Nations Demographic Yearbook,* New York, 1984.

      For cities:
Bombay – *Annual Report of the Executive Health Officer, 1980, 1981,* Bombay, 1985.
Manila – S.S. Basta, 'Nutrition and health in low income urban areas of the Third World', *Ecology of Food and Nutrition* Volume 6, 1977.
Porto Alegre – J.J. de Lima Guimaraes, A. Fischmann, cited in Figure 1.

**The contribution of malnutrition to such high death-rates in early childhood
has been clearly established.** For example, in 1973 the Pan-American Health
Organisation published the results of a major, hemisphere-wide study entitled
*Patterns of Mortality in Childhood*.[3] The study was conducted in ten countries
of the Western Hemisphere, and sought to investigate the multiple causes of
death in infants and children. The authors concluded that nutritional deficiency was the most important health problem associated with mortality in South
America: 57% of children under 5 years-of-age were found to have nutritional deficiency as an underlying or associated cause of death. It was found that
beyond the first month of life, there was a dramatic increase in the importance of malnutrition as an associated cause of death; this trend continued
through the second year and then gradually declined. Of even more importance, malnutrition as an underlying cause of death was found to increase
steadily throughout the first five years of life.

Is **severe** malnutrition associated with a greater risk of death than moderate or
mild malnutrition? This is an important question which has been addressed by
several studies in rural India and Bangladesh. For example, in a study carried
out in rural Matlab, Bangladesh, the nutritional status of around 2,000
children aged 0 to 23 months was recorded and the death-rate of these
children was assessed 12 months after the nutritional status measurements
were taken. The results of this study are presented in Table 3, and the vastly
increased risk of death for the most severely malnourished is well illustrated
in the final column.

**Table 3: Protein Energy Malnutrition and associated mortality over a 12-
month period.**

Location and date of survey: Rural Matlab, Bangladesh, 1975
Age-group of children: 0–23 months

| Method of measurement | Percentage of international reference | Percentage of deaths |
|---|---|---|
| Weight-for-age | 75% and over | 3.7 |
| | 60–75% | 4.2 |
| | 60% and under | 11.2 |
| Weight-for-height | 90% and over | 5.2 |
| | 80–90% | 5.3 |
| | 70–80% | 5.0 |
| | 70% and under | 14.7 |
| Height-for-age | 95% and over | 3.3 |
| | 90–95% | 3.9 |
| | 85–90% | 3.8 |
| | 85% and under | 11.3 |

Source: L.C. Chen *et al.*, 'Anthropometric assessment of Energy Protein Malnutrition
and subsequent risk of mortality among pre-school-aged children', *American
Journal of Clinical Nutrition* Volume 33 August, pp. 1836–1845, 1980.

**Increased risk of death is associated with severe malnutrition.** The extent of the risk is likely to vary depending upon the age of the child and the characteristics of the child's environment (such as disease patterns and feeding practices).

## 2.3.2. Malnutrition and the risk of disease

It is now well established that there is a close relationship between infection and malnutrition. **On the one hand, infections have been shown to lead to decreased rates of child growth as they impair appetite and hence food intake, digestion, absorption and metabolism of nutrients, thus affecting the efficiency with which a child makes use of his/her food.** Cultural feeding practices during periods of illness are also important, and it has been suggested, for example, that the tendency of the mother to withhold food is the largest contributor to the effect of illness on energy.

**On the other hand, malnutrition has been shown to lower the resistance of a child to infectious disease. In a moderately or severely malnourished child, infectious disease is often more prolonged, more severe, and has a higher rate of complications.**

The association between diarrhoea and malnutrition is a particular problem for young children. Several studies have emphasised the importance of nutrition as a determinant of the duration of diarrhoea. This is true for both moderate and severe malnutrition, whether expressed as a percentage of expected weight-for-age, height-for-age, or weight-for-height. The most comprehensive study in Bangladesh showed a graded increase in the duration of diarrhoea for all three anthropometric indicators: that is to say, **the duration of diarrhoea rises with an increase in the severity of malnutrition.[4] This is important because of the vicious circle that can develop when illness/malnutrition cause a further deterioration of nutritional status. The effect of diarrhoea on nutrient intake is a major feature in growth faltering of young children. The longer the duration of the disease, the longer it takes to get food intake back to normal.**

[3] R.R.Puffer, C.V.Serrano, *Patterns of Mortality in Childhood*, Pan-American Health Organisation, Scientific Publication No. 262, 1973.

[4] R.E. Black *et al.*, 'Malnutrition as a determining factor in diarrhoeal duration but not incidence among young children in a longitudinal study in rural Bangladesh' *American Journal of Clinical Nutrition* Volume 39, 1984.

Measles is another serious condition in severely malnourished children. Complications – including pneumonia, septicaemia and diarrhoea – are frequent, probably due to the lower resistance of the malnourished child. Several studies have documented the striking weight loss that often occurs during measles in young children. Differences in nutritional status would also explain the high case-fatality rate from measles in the Third World.

Among children in Europe and North America the fatality rate from measles is around 0.1 per 100 cases, whereas in rural Nigeria and Gambia rates of 7% and 14% respectively have been recorded.[5] In urban Natal in South Africa, a death rate of 26% has been recorded for children under 8 months-of-age.[6] Furthermore, studies in the Gambia have shown a steadily increasing death rate among children during the six months following an attack of measles.[7] Most of these deaths were from the complications of measles: chronic diarrhoea and pneumonia.

## 2.4. How is malnutrition measured in adults?

Nutritional status indicators are much less clearly defined for adults than for children, because of the concentration of research in the past on child health and nutrition. In adults, Body Mass Index (BMI) is used as an index of adult nutritional status; (BMI is weight in kilos divided by the square of height in metres, and is an index of leanness).

There is no generally accepted lower limit to BMI which is compatible with health. Indeed, studies have shown that the range of BMI measurements in different population groups vary; such variation could be due to, for example, genetic differences in the populations, or to differences in body fat or the process of adaptation to the environment in which the person grows up. Studies in Britain,[8] Norway[9] and the USA[10] have shown that the average BMI for these populations is around 22, and that those with a BMI below 20

[5] S.O. Foster, 'Immunizable and respiratory diseases and child mortality' Child survival strategies for research, *Population and Development Review*, supplement to Volume 10, pp. 119–140, 1984.

[6] W.E.K. Loening, H.M. Coovadia, 'Age specific recurrence rates of measles in urban, perio-urban and rural environments, implications for time of vaccine', *The Lancet* (ii), pp. 324–326, 1983.

[7] A. Tomkins, 'Protein Energy Malnutrition and the risk of infection'(mimeo), London School of Hygiene and Tropical Medicine, 1986.

[8] T.J. Cole *et al.*, 'Bronchitis, smoking and obesity in an English and a Danish town', *Bulletin de Physio-Pathologie Respiratoire* Volume 10:5, pp. 657–679, 1974.

[9] H.T. Waaler, 'Height, weight and mortality: the Norwegian experience', *Acta Medica Scandinavia* Supplement to No. 679, Stockholm, Sweden, 1984.

[10] A. Keys, 'Overweight, obesity, coronary heart disease and mortality', *Nutrition Review* Volume 38, pp. 297–306, 1980.

have a greater risk of mortality. Whereas studies in India and Java[11] have shown that the average BMI for these populations is lower than in Western populations and is around 19 or 20. For such populations it has been tentatively suggested by an international working party that a graded BMI classification of 16, 17 and 18.5 be used respectively as an index of severe, moderate and mild adult undernutrition.[12] Research on adult malnutrition indices is, however, in its infancy and there is at present little solid ground upon which to make decisions on cut-off points.

## 2.5. What is known about the consequences of malnutrition in adults?

### 2.5.1. Does maternal malnutrition affect birth weight?

Maternal nutrition during pregnancy is one of several factors which affect both the successful completion of pregnancy and the growth of the foetus. Other interacting factors include: age of the mother, her disease status, cigarette smoking, and her previous nutritional status as measured by stature. For example, chronic maternal malnutrition – often since childhood – may result in a small and sometimes abnormally-shaped pelvis, which has been found to be a contributory factor to the birth of infants of low birth weight and, in addition, can make childbirth a more dangerous process.

Under conditions of acute starvation, a relationship between current maternal malnutrition and low birth weight has been reported.[13] The evidence shows that **mothers who are currently severely malnourished are at risk of delivering low birth weight infants, which means that their infants face very high risks of morbidity and death, especially during the first year of life.**

The effect of less severe malnutrition on birth weight is not so clear cut. Some field studies have attempted to assess the effects of diet supplements for pregnant women on the birth weight of their infants. The results, after careful control of other interacting factors, indicate that in mothers who are severely malnourished, supplementation during pregnancy can improve birth weight. The average increase in birth weight, however, is generally small, and dependent upon the severity of malnourishment in the mother and the energy content of the supplement. The effect of supplementation is greater amongst those women who are **currently** either moderately or severely malnourished (as measured by rate of weight-gain during pregnancy).[14]

---

[11] P.B. Eveleth, J.M. Tanner, *Worldwide Variation in Human Growth*, Cambridge University Press, Cambridge, 1976.

[12] W.P.T. James, et al, 'Definition of chronic energy deficiency in adults', *European Journal of Clinical Nutrition*, Volume 42, pp. 969-981, 1988.

[13] C.A. Smith, 'Effects of maternal undernutrition upon new-born infants in Holland (1944-45)', *Journal of Pediatrics*, Volume 30, pp.229-243, 1947.

[14] A.M. Prentice *et al.*, 'Prenatal dietary supplementation of African women and birth-weight', *The Lancet* (i), p. 489, 1983.

## 2.5.2. Does maternal nutrition during lactation affect the quality and quantity of breast milk?

In the unhygienic living conditions common to many slums and shanty towns, breast-feeding is essential to protect the young infant from infection and malnutrition. It is generally assumed that production of breast milk is closely related to dietary intake during pregnancy and lactation, although there is at present very little reliable information available on either the quantity and quality of breast milk produced by nursing mothers or on how their milk is affected by their diet.

Field studies conducted in The Gambia,[15] Mexico[16] and India[17] found that the quantity of breast milk was more related to the weight of the infant at birth than to the dietary intake of the mother during lactation. The provision of dietary supplements to lactating women did not lead to any significant increase in the quantity of breast milk produced or to the energy or protein content of the breast milk. The vitamin and mineral content of breast milk can, however, be increased by vitamin and mineral supplementation and hence reflects the diet of lactating women.

**These findings suggest that the nutritional status of the mother during pregnancy not only affects the growth of the foetus, but also may determine the lactation capacity of the mothers.** Mothers who are sufficiently nourished during pregnancy to produce infants of good birth weight are also likely to produce more milk. Mothers who are less well nourished are more likely to deliver small babies and produce less milk. Low birth-weight infants may need encouragement to suckle more frequently so as to increase their mother's milk supply.

## 2.5.3. Does malnutrition in labouring adults affect working capacity, productivity and earning capacity?

There is now evidence from several developing countries that children who are malnourished and poor grow up to be shorter and often thinner adults. Adult nutritional status is therefore an outcome of past and present nutrition.

In developing countries where mechanisation is at a minimum, it is human labour which provides the power for productive economic work. Work capacity, performance and productivity of workers is therefore potentially important for income with which to buy food and for food production itself, at both the household and national levels.

---

[15] A.M. Prentice et al., 'Dietary supplementation of Gambian nursing mothers and lactation performance', The Lancet (ii), p.886, 1980.

[16] A. Chavez et al., 'Child nutrition problems during lactation in poor rural areas', Proceedings of IXth International Congress of Nutrition, Krager, Volume 2, p.90, 1975.

[17] C. Gopolan, 'Studies on lactation in poor Indian communities', Journal of Tropical Pediatrics, Volume 4, p.87, 1958.

Is there any evidence that malnutrition in labouring adults affects working capacity or productivity? A number of studies which have been conducted in various developing countries indicate that where work is labour-intensive, unmechanised and physically strenuous, undernourished adults have a decreased working capacity compared with well-nourished adults and they may also have a lower productivity per unit of labour.

Another dimension of this problem is illustrated by a study from India suggesting that better-nourished agricultural workers are **selected** for physically strenuous work and are paid far higher wages than undernourished workers, who are **selected** because of their low body-weight for work entailing light physical activity.[18]   The wages earned by these agricultural labourers were found to be directly related to body-weight. Classification of subjects according to earnings and age revealed that better-paid groups not only weighed significantly more, but had better nutritional status when they were under 5 years old. **It would thus appear that poor nutritional status in childhood, which has been shown to lead to low adolescent body-weight and work capacity, can also be associated with lower earnings in manual labour.**

## 2.6. The Family Health Profile: indicators of household nutritional status

In developing countries, child nutritional status measurements are often used as indirect indicators of the nutritional status of whole households or communities. A major problem of using child nutritional status measurements in this way, however, remains that of determining whether disease or food shortage caused the malnutrition in the first place. Such a distinction is important if appropriate interventions are to be accurately and efficiently targeted.

A way of enhancing the usefulness of nutritional status indicators for policy purposes is to take the weight and height of all household members. It is then possible to distinguish patterns which characterise different types of problems and causes. Table 4 illustrates some of the many patterns that might be found.

---

[18] K. Satyanarayana *et al.*, 'Agricultural employment, wage earnings and nutritional status of teenage rural Hyderabad boys', *Indian Journal of Nutrition and Dietetics*, Volume 17, 1980.

Of course, family patterns other than those shown in Table 4 are possible and each could be interpreted as a result of specific family problems. Malnutrition and disease tend to cluster in problem families. When such families are identified and the pattern of their needs determined, interventions can be more usefully targeted. Anthropometry has its limitations and cannot detect all diseases, but it will increase efficiency in the use of field data for action programmes.

**Table 4: Some patterns of malnutrition in families.**

| | | | | Present nutritional status of: | | | | |
|---|---|---|---|---|---|---|---|---|
| *Pattern | Father | Mother | Infant | Pre-school child | | School child | | |
| | | | | (No. 1) | (No. 2) | (No. 1) | (No. 2) | (No. 3) |
| A | + | + | + | + | NA | + | + | NA |
| B | + | + | + | O | O | + | + | NA |
| C | + | + | O | O | NA | + | NA | NA |
| D | + | O | O | O | NA | + | + | NA |
| E | O | O | O | O | O | O | NA | NA |
| F | + | + | + | + | NA | + | O | + |

*Key*
\+ : weight-for-height or BMI is satisfactory
O : weight-for-height or BMI below critical level
NA : no family member

*Notes*
Pattern A: shows that current nutritional status of all family members is adequate. The parents and older children may be small in stature, reflecting under-nutrition in early childhood, but their present nutritional status is satisfactory.
Pattern B: the adults, infants and older children are all adequately nourished, but the pre-school children show evidence of present malnutrition. This is a common pattern in poor communities, where infants are generally protected for the first few months of life by breast-feeding, but from the later months of infancy to about four years of age the children are under-nourished. By the time children reach school age they can cope with their environment adequately, although they may be short in stature. This pattern of malnutrition does not reflect an absolute deficiency of food or inadequate child-care (as when parents are forced to work, leaving young children in the care of their older siblings).
Pattern C: suggests poor practices of infant and child-care, perhaps with a working mother who cannot feed and care for her younger children during the day.
Pattern D: poor nutrition and disease in the mother is almost certainly the primary factor leading to secondary effects in the younger children. The school-age children can fend for themselves.
Pattern E: indicates an absolute lack of food in the family.
Pattern F: with isolated 'malnutrition' of a school-age child, is much more likely to result from disease than malnutrition.
Source: A.E. Dugdale, 'Family anthropometry: a new strategy for determining community nutrition', *The Lancet*, September 21, pp. 672–673, 1985.

# CHAPTER 3.

# CAUSES OF MALNUTRITION – ANALYSIS OF THE INDIVIDUAL, THE HOUSEHOLD, THE COMMUNITY AND THE STATE

## 3.1. Developing a framework for an analysis of causes of malnutrition

Many inter-related factors are known to affect the nutritional status of an individual, family or community. Socio-economic and political forces, household factors and individual characteristics may all interact to contribute to the state of an individual's malnourishment.

In order to understand the multiple causes of urban malnutrition, we need a method for analysing the factors that are known to affect nutritional status and the way in which they interact. One way of classifying factors that affect the nutritional status of individuals is by the social level at which they act; for example, to identify factors that act at the individual level, at the household level and at the community and national levels.

The framework is also relevant in deciding on the kinds of programmes and policies that are most likely to have an effect on malnutrition, and in assessing whether existing projects and policies attempt to attack the **symptoms** or **underlying causes** of malnutrition.

In our framework we will trace what is known about multiple causes of malnutrition in children under 5 in urban areas from the level of the individual through to the household, community and national levels. It should be emphasised that social, economic and political forces vary between continents, countries and cities, so it is impossible to generalise about the precise nature of the multiple causes of malnutrition.

# The Framework

## 3.2. Level One: the individual

At the level of the individual, factors that affect growth and functioning of the child under 5 include birth weight and the fulfilment of nutritional requirements during growth. The former is partly determined by the health and nutritional status of the mother (see Chapter 2). Clearly, low birth weight infants face very high risks of disease and death.

The fulfilment of nutritional requirements during growth is determined by nutrient intake and the health of the child.

### 3.2.1. Nutritional and health problems faced by infants during the weaning period

During the first years of life children grow and develop very rapidly. The amounts of energy and nutrients needed to sustain this growth are, when adjusted for body-weight, proportionately higher for infants than for older children (see Table 5); a 1-year-old child, for example, normally needs an energy intake around two-and-a-half times greater than her 7-year-old sister (per kilogram of body-weight per day).

It is well established that breast milk is best for infants. Much has been written about its advantages in comparison with substitutes derived from animal milk: it is readily available, especially if the child is fed on demand; and it has valuable anti-infective properties, which is especially important, as a newborn infant is very vulnerable to disease-causing organisms due to the inadequacy of the underdeveloped body defence system.

**Table 5: Nutritional requirements during infancy and childhood.**

|  | AGE | | |
|---|---|---|---|
|  | 0–5 months | 6–11 months | 12–35 months |
| Energy (Kcal/Kg/day) | 120 | 110 | 100 |
| Protein (g/Kg/day) | 2.2 | 2.1 | 1.8 |

Source: D. Nabarro et al., 'Studying weaning: a guide for workers in health, welfare and development programmes' (mimeo), London School of Hygiene and Tropical Medicine, 1984.

Exclusive breast-feeding has been shown to be nutritionally satisfactory for the infant for the first 4-6 months of life; thereafter, faltering in the pattern of growth begins and food supplements are necessary. However, it is during this period when foods and milks other than breast milk are introduced (weaning) that children are most vulnerable to infection and malnutrition. In fact, the period when children's health is most in danger begins at around 4-6 months and lasts until they are fully able to feed themselves, perhaps when they are about 3 years old.

During this period, there are several feeding practices which have an influence on child nutrition. One is the age at which supplementation begins. Another is the method of food preparation. Foods prepared at home – whether out of a tin or home-made – frequently become contaminated with bacteria from the water supply or the domestic environment. Furthermore, feeding utensils, such as bottles and teats, also become heavily contaminated. This problem is particularly severe in urban slum settlements. The situation is made even worse if food is prepared in advance (perhaps because the mother has other domestic or employment responsibilities, or to economise in fuel) and kept for long periods while the bacteria multiply. The result is often diarrhoea which can quickly lead to dehydration and death. A third factor relates to the nutrient density of the food. When weaning (introducing solid food in addition to breast milk) begins, the food must be soft. In practice food is often mixed with large volumes of water, especially if mothers come from poor families and are unable to afford additions of high energy-dense foods such as fats and oils. In such circumstances, but especially during illness when appetite falls, small children need to be fed frequently during the day, which is very time-consuming, and can be especially difficult for mothers from poor families who may have other domestic and economic responsibilities.

**The weaning period is thus a particularly dangerous time for infants, and those in a position to advise are faced with a life-threatening dilemma: if breast-feeding is supplemented at an early age, infection is likely, because of the severe problem of contamination which can lead to diarrhoea and death. Alternatively, if supplementation is delayed, the child's growth falters and he/she can become malnourished, which often aggravates the outcome of disease and increases the risk of death.**

### 3.2.2. How are infants' nutritional requirements met in urban areas?

Breast-feeding patterns vary enormously throughout the world, depending upon region and location (i.e. urban or rural). World Fertility Survey data collected in 42 developing countries indicate that, in general, breast-feeding is more prevalent and of longer duration in Asia than in Latin America. The data also show that the **prevalence and duration of breast-feeding are lower in urban areas than in rural areas in the same country.** However, regional differences in the duration of breast-feeding in urban areas are very marked:

for example, it is worth noting that breast-feeding is more prolonged in urban areas of many Asian countries than in rural areas of many Latin American countries (see Table 6).

Within urban areas of the same country, differences in the prevalence and duration of breast-feeding are also evident between different socio-economic groups. For example, surveys conducted in Kenya, Mexico and Malaysia in 1979 show that the prevalence and duration of breast-feeding are higher amongst the urban poor than amongst the urban elite (Table 7). The consequences of diminished prevalence and duration of breast-feeding, however, are

**Table 6: Mean duration of breast-feeding (in months) in different regions of the world.**

| Region/country | RURAL | URBAN |
|---|---|---|
| ASIA | | |
| Indonesia | 25.3 | 15.9 |
| Bangladesh | 29.2 | 25.5 |
| Thailand | 20.3 | 9.7 |
| AFRICA | | |
| Kenya | 16.2 | 12.0 |
| Senegal | 19.4 | 16.7 |
| AMERICAS | | |
| Peru | 17.0 | 10.6 |
| Mexico | 11.5 | 6.7 |
| Dominican Republic | 10.9 | 6.1 |

Source: B. Ferry and D. Smith, 'Breast-feeding differentials, comparative studies, cross-national summaries', *World Fertility Survey*, London 1983.

**Table 7: Percentage of mothers breast-feeding, classified by social status.**

| | Age of infant | | | | | | | | |
|---|---|---|---|---|---|---|---|---|---|
| | at birth | | | 5–6 months | | | 10–12 months | | |
| Social group | Kenya | Mexico | Malaysia | Kenya | Mexico | Malaysia | Kenya | Mexico | Malaysia |
| Urban Elite | 98 | 80 | 68 | 79 | 17 | 11 | 54 | 6 | 4 |
| Urban Poor | 98 | 85 | 75 | 85 | 46 | 30 | 80 | 26 | 24 |
| Rural | 100 | 91 | 85 | 99 | 53 | 65 | 86 | 37 | 54 |

Source: H.J. Dimond, A. Ashworth, 'Infant feeding practices in Kenya, Mexico and Malaysia' (mimeo), London School of Hygiene and Tropical Medicine, 1986.

likely to be far worse for children of the urban poor than for those of the urban elite, because of the dangers of contamination and over-dilution of weaning foods.

### 3.2.3. What evidence is there on the dangers of early weaning?

Historical studies from the first half of this century in the USA showed there was a higher death-rate associated with early weaning, which persisted through the first year of life.

Similar but more recent data from developing countries is shown in Table 8. These data are derived from the Pan-American Health Organisation study of mortality in early childhood. They indicate that children who were breast-fed for less than six months are between six and fourteen times more likely to die at 6 to 11 months-of-age than children who were breast-fed for six months or longer. More evidence comes from a slum in Cité Simone in Port au Prince, Haiti, where children who are bottle-fed in the first month of life face a four-fold increased risk of death at 18 months, compared with those who are exclusively breast-fed in the first month of life.[19]

**Table 8: The relationship between breast-feeding and infant mortality in four PAHO study areas around 1970.**

| Study area | Percent of infants breast-fed | | Percent breast-fed among infants dying at 6–11 months | | Ratio of mortality risk at 6–11 months of those breast-fed less than 6 months to those breast-fed at least 6 months |
|---|---|---|---|---|---|
| | Less than 6 months | At least 6 months | Less than 6 months | At least 6 months | |
| El Salvador | 20 | 20 | 78.9 | 22.0 | 14.2:1 |
| Kingston, Jamaica | 51 | 49 | 87.4 | 12.6 | 7.1:1 |
| Medellin, Colombia | 61.8 | 31.2 | 91.3 | 8.8 | 6.4:1 |
| Sao Paulo, Brazil | 77.2 | 22.8 | 95.9 | 4.1 | 6.8:1 |

Source: J.D. Wray, 'Maternal nutrition, breast-feeding and infant survival', *Nutrition and Human Reproduction* W.M. Mosely (ed.), Plenum Press, New York, 1977.

[19] R. Boulos *et al.*, 'Cité Simone, an urban slum of Haiti: the malnutrition challenge'. Paper presented at the workshop on Community Health and the Urban Poor, organised in Oxford by the London School of Hygiene and Tropical Medicine, Oxfam and UNICEF, 7-12th July 1985.

Similar conclusions relating to the increased prevalence of malnutrition in bottle-fed compared with breast-fed infants are shown in Table 9. These results are taken from a random sample survey of 136 infants from poor urban families in Port Moresby in Papua New Guinea in 1975/76. Over one-third of the infants seen were artifically fed, out of whom 69% were malnourished, compared with 26% of breast-fed infants. **The risk of being severely malnourished (i.e. less than 60% weight-for-age) was over seven times greater for bottle-fed than for breast-fed infants.**

Further suggestive evidence of the very high rates of malnutrition associated with early weaning and disease is illustrated by data collected during 1970/71 in the slums of Bangkok (see Figure 2). Here it was found that severe malnutrition was occurring at a much earlier age in the urban slums than in rural areas in Thailand.

---

**This section on the individual level of analysis has shown how feeding practices and illness interact with the child's physical development to determine his/her nutritional status. The importance of breast-feeding and the hygienic preparation of weaning foods in a harmful slum environment has been stressed.**

---

## 3.3. Level Two: the household

At the level of the individual, the child's nutritional status is dependent upon food, nutrient intake and disease. These immediate determinants of malnutrition, however, are strongly influenced by constraints that act upon and affect the whole household.

### 3.3.1. The effect of household economy on the nutritional status of young children

In urban areas it is often the case that only a small proportion of the population living in slums and shanty towns are lucky enough to find permanent and secure employment which provides a stable source of income. Others may own productive assets such as equipment and tools and have financial capital, so that they can set themselves up as traders or self-employed skilled craftsmen, such as tailors, carpenters, etc. Many, however, neither have access to permanent secure employment nor own productive or financial resources; they exist on a day-to-day basis seeking casual employment.

### 3.3.2. The insecurity of employment

In countries with abundant labour, casual employment is often insecure and income low and unstable. The proportion of casual workers to the total work-force varies in slums and shanty towns, and will partly depend upon the

**Table 9: Nutritional status of infants in Port Moresby, Papua New Guinea.**

| | Group 1 Breast-fed infants | Group 2 Artificially fed infants |
|---|---|---|
| Number of infants seen | 88 | 48 |
| Number between 80% and 60% of standard weight-for-age | 20 (23%) | 22 (46%) |
| Number below 60% of standard weight-for-age | 3 ( 3%) | 11 (23%) |
| Total number below 80% of standard weight-for-age | 23 (26%) | 33 (69%) |

Source: J. Lambert, J. Barford, 'Port Moresby infant feeding survey', *Papua New Guinea Medical Journal* Volume 20:4, 1977.

**Figure 2: Rates of malnutrition in the urban slums of Bangkok, Thailand, around 1972.**

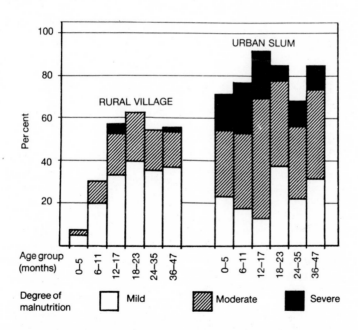

Source: J.D. Wray, 'Nutrition and health in urban slums: an overview', paper presented at the workshop on Community Health and the Urban Poor, organised by LSHTM, Oxfam and UNICEF, Oxford, 1985.

degree of industrialisation of the city and country concerned. In a slum in Asia in 1984, for example (see Section 4.4), 63% of household principal earners were casual workers, 34% were self-employed traders and only 3% held permanent secure employment. Furthermore, when these households were classified by monthly income, the poorest 25% consisted almost entirely of casual workers, whereas the richest 25% were almost entirely self-employed traders. The average total monthly income of the richest 25% in the slum was nearly eight times that of the poorest 25%, even after taking into account family size and composition. Similar proportions of stable, casual and self-employed workers were found in three slums in the city of Chimbote, Peru in 1980/82 (Table 10), whereas slightly higher proportions of permanent wage-earners were found in slum studies in Coimbatore, Tamil Nadu, India in 1980 (Table 11).

**Table 10: Occupations of household earners in slums in Chimbote, Peru (1980–82).**

| Shanty town | Economically active population | | Employment | | |
| | | | Stable | Unemployed and casual labourers | Self-employed |
|---|---|---|---|---|---|
| Miraflores | No. | 1,289 | 202 | 940 | 147 |
| Bajo | % | 100 | 15.6 | 72.9 | 11.5 |
| Señor de los | No. | 588 | 101 | 384 | 103 |
| Milagros | % | 100 | 17.1 | 65.3 | 17.5 |
| Coishco | No. | 5,237 | 976 | 3,659 | 602 |
| | % | 100 | 18.6 | 69.9 | 11.5 |

Source: *Self-Census in three shanty towns*, Centre for Family Education, Chimbote, Peru, 1980–82.

**Table 11: Occupations of household earners in slums in Coimbatore, India.**

| Type of employment | Number of earners | Percentage distribution |
|---|---|---|
| Permanent wage workers | 141 | 17 |
| Casual wage workers | 397 | 48 |
| Self-employed workers | 238 | 29 |
| Others (including unemployed, beggars, agricultural labour) | 50 | 6 |
| | 826 | 100 |

Source: J. Harriss, 'Character of an urban economy — small-scale production and labour markets in Coimbatore', *Economic and Political Weekly* (Bombay), 12 June 1982.

The pressing need to increase the family income forces many children to abandon school to contribute to the household. A 1978 study of 10 slums in Bombay, India, for example, found that children under 14 years old constituted a substantial proportion of the total labour force. Many of these children worked very long hours: 15% worked 10-14 hours daily and 40% worked 6-10 hours daily. The situation has not changed. **Wage rates are low and the children often work under appalling conditions, with consequent severe repercussions on their health and nutritional status, and upon their emotional and mental development.**

**Young mothers are increasingly compelled to leave small children and infants and go out in search of work, which can expose young babies to further risk of malnutrition in poor households because of the inability of the family to provide adequate care in the mother's absence,** as will be discussed later. The discrimination against women in terms of equal pay for equal work, and their exclusion from higher-paid jobs, make the provision of a sufficient family diet even more remote, especially for the many single and abandoned mothers who are the sole breadwinners of their families.

There are, in fact, more single mothers in cities than is usually realised, and they may be the most vulnerable and easily neglected group among the urban poor and malnourished. For instance, some studies in slum areas in Latin American cities have shown that nearly a third of the households are headed by single mothers. Even in Asia (where the proportion of such women seems to be lower) large numbers of abandoned mothers may easily go uncounted because they have been forced to live by the roadside with their children and are not to be found in the more organised slum settlements.

**The consequences of a few days' unemployment are very serious for the urban poor and can represent a crushing financial blow.** For example, for a casual labourer, three days lost per month due to diarrhoeal disease corresponds to a 12–15% loss of monthly income; and reduced productivity from chronic or sub-acute illness such as anaemia, bronchitis, tuberculosis, or from malnutrition would contribute to a further lowering of work potential and earnings. Basta (1977)[20] estimates that decreased work ability and earnings associated with such illnesses can be at least 25% of monthly income, not taking into account further income losses aggravated by having to pay for medicines, doctors, transport to clinics, interest payments on debts incurred to cover these expenses, and the cost of food for the household. Severe illness can therefore be financially crippling and often pushes families deeper into debt.

The financial repercussions of adult ill-health are likely to have serious consequences on child nutrition. Furthermore, adults who are ill and/or malnourished are very likely to be unable to cope with the time-intensive demands of child-care. In a slum study in Bangladesh, the relative risk of a

---

[20] S. Basta, 'Nutrition and health in low income urban areas of the Third World', *Ecology of Food and Nutrition,* Volume 6, pp. 113-124, 1977.

severely malnourished child coming from a household with an incapacitated earner was two and a half times greater than from households without an incapacitated earner.[21]

Although the resourcefulness of the poor is extraordinary, they are nevertheless locked into a trap of low capital, low training, shortage of working opportunities and low income. They are often kept down in this position by fear of unemployment or by the complex dependency relationships created by their employers and social superiors. Studies conducted in slums in Pune, India in 1976 and 1980, for example, indicate that only a minority succeed in breaking out of the vicious circle of poverty. A resurvey in 1988 found that some of those households had slipped back into poverty once again, underlining the vulnerability of the urban poor.[22]

Because they lack assets and savings, poor urban households are vulnerable to the expenses of any crisis, which could have severe repercussions on the nutrition of young children. There are many other crises besides adult ill-health which could have serious effects on child nutrition, including: death of a household earner; a husband deserting his wife and children; imprisonment of a household member; increases in rent, or in the price of food, fuel and other basic necessities; the landlord's insistence on payment of rent arrears, or similar demands from other creditors; exorbitant dowry demands by the prospective groom for the marriage of one of the daughters; or a landlord, labour lord or employer insisting that their tenants or employees help to finance a display of fairy lights for the visit of a prominent politician or foreign visitor.

### 3.3.3. Demands on the household budget

Patterns of household expenditure usually reflect the level and stability of income. It is frequently stated that the income of the urban poor is greater than that of the rural poor. If this is the case, however, higher income for the urban poor does not necessarily imply increased food intake and better nutritional status. This is because the cost-of-living in the city is often higher than in rural areas. In addition to food, cooking fuel and lighting have to be paid for, and in some instances even utilities such as water. There are also the costs of house rental, and other basic necessities such as clothing, education and transport. Creditors may arrive demanding payments on debts incurred due to lack of income to buy food or to meet medical or ceremonial expenses, and these debt payments, together with their interest, have to be met. In the Asian slum mentioned previously, 64% of the households in the poorest income group were indebted to cover the cost of food alone – and to a level which was **on average** 75% of their monthly income; whereas no households in the richest income group were indebted to cover the cost of food.

[21] J. Pryer, 'When breadwinners fall ill; preliminary findings from a case study in Bangladesh', *IDS Bulletin*, Volume 20, No. 2, pp. 49-56, 1989.

[22] M. Bapat *et al.*, *'The impact of environment and economic class on health in urban India; case studies of Pune and Durgapur'*, (mimeo), SOAS, 1989.

Thus for the casually employed, the day's earnings are soon gone on that day's expenses, and usually there is only enough to buy the smallest quantities of food. Buying food daily in small quantities, rather than more cheaply in bulk, is an added expense for the urban poor. In a Latin American city, for example, a study revealed that 64% of the slum dwellers and 97% of the shanty town dwellers could not reach a main market, where food prices are cheaper, without using public transport – an investment often too high in relation to the little that they have to spend.[23] As a result they are often dependent upon small shopkeepers and street vendors who may offer a more limited range and quality of food at higher prices. **The price that the urban poor therefore end up paying for food can be much higher than that paid by middle class shoppers at central markets, especially if they are forced to take credit from the shopkeeper because they have no money.**

It is true that widespread starvation is unlikely in the larger urban localities, at least in peace-time. Migrants from areas where the harvest has failed will often head for large cities in the knowledge that, at a time of crisis, food will usually be channelled into urban areas, and to some·extent it will get distributed to destitute households. But these are very different circumstances from those that give rise to persistent malnutrition. Even where there is a system of fair-price shops or other means of distributing food subsidised by the State, the poorest (and especially the recent migrants) often do not easily get access to such a system. Lack of knowledge of its existence or how to gain access to it, ineligibility to register (due to migrant status), or insufficient resources to make initial payments (especially where access requires bribery), are all likely to hinder the poorest households. The evidence that inadequate food intake is widespread in urban areas confirms that access to sufficient food day-by-day is not assured at all.

### 3.3.4. Low and unstable incomes increase the risk of malnourishment

Except under highly controlled conditions, it is difficult to obtain reliable information on the food intake of individuals: there are problems in estimating both the quantity and the nutritional content of the food consumed, and then in interpreting consumption in relation to nutritional needs. Nevertheless, food consumption studies in different groups of the same population can indicate overall trends. For example, studies of food consumption patterns amongst different socio-economic groups within cities consistently show that the average food energy intake is much lower for the poor than for the middle and higher income groups, as is the case in rural areas. It must also be remembered that the low average intakes for the poor conceal wide variations within groups, and that 50% are getting **less** than this average.

---

[23] J. Nelson, P.E. Mandl, 'Peri-urban malnutrition, a neglected problem', *Carnets de l'Enfance*, Volume 43, pp. 25-46, 1978.

In Lima, Peru in 1978, for example, whilst upper class families consumed **on average** 20% **more** calories than the World Health Organisation recommends, the average consumption of poor families was 20% **below** the WHO recommendations.[24] Occupational and income class variations are also shown for 13 major cities in India (Table 12). In this study, comparisons are made with food intake data from a range of socio-economic groups in rural areas. These figures strongly imply that **the nutritional situation for the urban poor is no better than that of the rural poor.**

Patterns of food purchase and consumption amongst the poor not only reflect the cost of other basic necessities for living, but may also be influenced by the amount of time household adults – especially women – spend in income-earning activities. Because women are short of time, and because fuel is costly, many poor families are forced to rely on ready-made or easy-to-prepare foods, which are usually expensive. Household surveys in Indonesia and the Philippines, for example, found that in urban areas households spend on average 25% of their food budgets on snacks bought from street vendors,

**Table 12: Food intake data from 13 major cities in India, with a rural comparison, 1974–79.**

| Mean kilo-calorie intakes (per CU per day) | | | | |
|---|---|---|---|---|
| Urban | 1 | 2 | Rural | |
| High income group | 2000–3085 | 2600 | 10 acre land-holding | 2375–3100 |
| | | | 5–10 acre land-holding | 2100–2860 |
| | | | Landless | 1865–2310 |
| Middle income group | 1880–2715 | 2365 | | |
| Low income group | 1760–2665 | 2230 | | |
| Industrial labour | 1900–2510 | 2245 | | |
| Slum dwellers | 1760–2290 | 2010 | Harijans | 1600–2460 |

*Key:* 1 = range of means for various cities
2 = pooled average for the group
CU = nutritional consumption unit based on the recommended daily kilo-calorie intake of a moderately active man

Source: K.S. Jaya Rao, 'Urban nutrition in India — 1' *Bulletin of the Nutrition Foundation of India* Volume 6:4, 1985.

---

[24] ENAPROM (1978), 'Encuesta Nacional de Hogares de Propositos Multiples', quoted in Sigma One Corporation, *Un analisis de la situacion alimentaria - nutricional en el Peru*, 1983.

and in Senegal it was 20%.[25] **Food habits amongst the poor may also be heavily influenced by the advertising of Western imported foods and the consumption patterns of the rich.** The frequently reported increased consumption of imported baby milks and foods, biscuits and Coca Cola are good examples of this; not only are such foods often deficient in specific nutrients, but their relatively high cost may reduce further the purchase of more nutritious foods.

Several studies have looked at neighbourhood differences in the prevalence of malnutrition. These studies indicate that **malnutrition tends to be concentrated in neighbourhoods where poor families live.** The national nutrition survey of Peru carried out in 1972 found that 19% of children under 6 years old in metropolitan Lima were malnourished; that figure rose to 24% in low socio-economic groups. A study carried out in one of the shanty towns in Southern Lima in 1978 found that 28% of children under 6 were malnourished, with a higher percentage of severely malnourished children than in previous studies (Table 13). Similarly, results from a study in Nagpur in the State of Maharashtra, India, between 1975 and 1980, indicate that there is a

**Table 13: Nutritional status of pre-school children from contrasting studies in Lima, Peru, 1972–78.**

| Study | Percentage Normal | Percentage malnourished Grade 1 | Grade 2 | Grade 3 | Total percentage malnourished |
|---|---|---|---|---|---|
| ENCA 1972 Metropolitan Lima | 81 | 17 | 2 | 0 | 19 |
| ENCA 1972 Low socio-economic group | 76 | 21 | 3 | 0 | 24 |
| Anderson et al. 1978 Flora Tristan shanty town | 72 | 20 | 8 | | 28 |

**Source:** J.M. Anderson et al., 'Child-care in urban and rural Peru' (mimeo), June 1978, cited in Ministerio de Economica y Finanzas, *Niveles de Vida: analisis de la situacion alimenticia en el Peru*, ENCA, 1972.

[25] M. Cohen, *The Urban Street Food Trade*, Equity Policy Centre, Washington DC, USA, 1984.

greater concentration of child malnutrition in the slums in this city, especially when compared with medium income groups: 68% of children aged 1–5 years in the slums were moderately or severely malnourished compared with 22% in the medium income group (see Figure 3). Another study conducted in a slum in Bombay in 1984/85 found that **within slum localities, child malnutrition is concentrated in the poorest households** (see Table 14).

**Table 14: Percentage distribution of child malnutrition in Dharavi slum, Bombay, 1984–85.**

| Socio-economic status | Nutritional status (weight-for-age) % distribution | | | | |
|---|---|---|---|---|---|
| | % of international reference | | | | Total |
| | over 90 | 75–90 | 60–75 | under 60 | |
| Low | 42 | 39 | 15 | 4 | 100 |
| Medium | 53 | 30 | 14 | 3 | 100 |
| High | 63 | 25 | 10 | 1 | 100 |
| Overall% | 53 | 31 | 13 | 3 | 100 |

Source: The Dharavi Project, 'Final report on an investigation of infant feeding patterns in the major urban slum of Dharavi, Bombay' (mimeo), Dept. of Preventative and Social Medicine, L.T. Medical College, Bombay, and Edinburgh Royal Infirmary, 1985.

### 3.3.5. Child malnutrition – due to poverty or ignorance?

A common explanation for child malnourishment is that the child's mother does not know how to make the best use of the foods at her disposal. According to this theory, the answer lies in nutrition education for the mother so that she is then able to feed her child properly. **Whilst not denying the importance of education – especially in urban areas where new food habits develop – it is important not to lose sight of the root causes of malnutrition which lie firmly embedded in the unequal distribution of resources both nationally and internationally.**

For example, a detailed nutrition study carried out in 1973 and 1980 in the shanty towns of Pamplona in the south of Lima, Peru, showed that poor women did know how to adjust the family menu according to the availability and price of foods, and how to make the most of their scarce resources. As inflation eroded purchasing power between 1973 and 1980, women changed the composition of the family diet; **the changes made were nutritionally**

# Figure 3: Percentage distribution of children (1–5 yrs) in Nagpur (Maharashtra) according to grades of malnutrition (1975–80).

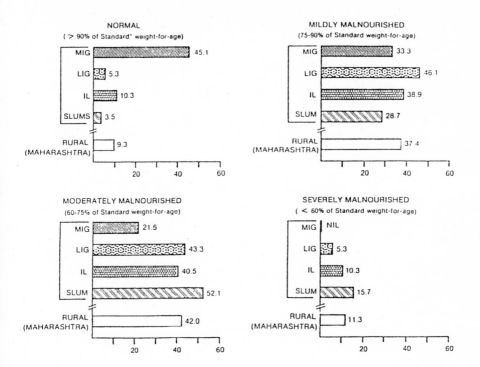

Key: Standard: well-to-do Indian children

MIG: middle income group (including junior civil servants, junior college lecturers, etc.)

LIG: low income group (including lowest grade public employees)

IL: industrial labour

SLUM: slum inhabitants

Source: *Nutrition News,* National Institute of Nutrition (Hyderabad), Volume 7:3, 1986. (Data from National Nutrition Monitoring Bureau, India.)

appropriate and allowed the total calorie consumption to be maintained (see Table 15). However, this adaptation for survival clearly has its limits. With the drastic decline in the purchasing power of wages and the steeply rising prices of food in Peru in the period 1980–85, it is unlikely that the women were able to *continue* to adjust the family menu to maintain a nutritionally adequate diet. Clearly, low effective income is a primary determinant of low food intake.

**Table 15: Changes in dietary composition between 1973 and 1980 in Pamplona, Peru.**

| Dietary characteristics | 1973 | 1980 |
|---|---|---|
| % calorific requirement fulfilled | 91 | 91 |
| Selected sources of calories: | | |
| % calories from protein sources | 10 | 9 |
| % calories from fat sources | 21 | 15 |
| % calories from cereals | 46 | 49 |
| % calories from potatoes | 4 | 5 |
| Sources of protein: | | |
| % protein from animal sources | 30 | 21 |
| % protein from non-animal sources | 70 | 79 |

Source: Adapted from H. Creed Kanashiro, 'El consumo de alimentos en grupos urbanos de bajos ingresos', *Agricultura y Alimentación: bases de un nuevo enfoque*, M. Lajo *et al.* (eds.), Lima, Peru, 1982; and H. Creed Kanashiro, G. Graham, 'Changes over time in food intakes of a migrated population' in 'Malnutrition: determinants and consequences', P. L. White, N. Selvey (eds.), *Current Topics in Nutrition and Disease* Volume 10, p. 198, LISS, New York, 1984.

### 3.3.6. The effect of maternal employment on breast-feeding patterns

Maternal employment is widely cited as a major reason for the general decline of breast-feeding, especially in urban areas. Yet a review of 82 major studies on infant-feeding conducted throughout the world found that women themselves seldom gave employment as a reason for terminating breast-feeding.[26]

To understand the relationship between women's work and breast-feeding, an important distinction should be made between work that requires the regular sustained separation of mother and infant, and work that does not. In a traditional rural setting, women's work is often compatible with breast-feeding and other aspects of child-care. In the urban context, however, this may not always be the case.

---

[26] P. Van Esterik, T. Greiner, 'Breast-feeding and women's work: constraints and opportunities', *Studies in Family Planning*, Volume 12, No. 4, pp. 184-197, 1981.

In a study in the Philippines, the breast-feeding behaviour of working and non-working mothers was observed in four different ecological settings: an urban squatter settlement and an urban *barrio* (neighbourhood) in Cebu city, and in rural coastal and rural hinterland regions.[27] In all four communities, breast-feeding declined with a rise in socio-economic status, but it was lowest in prevalence in the urban squatter settlements. Amongst working mothers in general it was found that where women worked close to home they were able to breast-feed their children; however, there was a highly significant decline in breast-feeding when the mother worked a long way from home, whereas in the squatter settlements, where breast-feeding was lowest, most of the women worked in the same vicinity and employment appeared to have a minimal effect on their breast-feeding behaviour.

Compatibility of the mother's employment is therefore a determinant of breast-feeding patterns; but it is not the only determinant. The authors of the Philippines study were unable to explain the reasons behind the lower breast-feeding prevalence in the urban squatter settlements. On the other hand, the decline of breast-feeding associated with a rise in socio-economic status has been attributed to the effect of multi-national corporation advertising, which is designed to undermine women's self-confidence and foster aspirations towards what is supposed to be Western behaviour. Unsuitable hospital practices and advice given by medical and para-medical personnel are also much to blame.

### 3.3.7. The effect of maternal employment on child nutritional status

There is certainly some evidence that children from poor families who have working mothers may suffer from increased levels of malnutrition, although little research has been done on this subject. For example, a study conducted in 1979 in two poor urban neighbourhoods in Kingston, Jamaica found that amongst 309 children under 4 years old, the nutritional status of those with working mothers was lower than that of those whose mothers did not work.[28] But in that study the degree of statistical correlation was weak and, as in similar studies, the economic status of the household was not controlled. It may well be that households with working mothers are inherently poorer than those where the mother is able to stay at home.

Two separate issues have to be considered when looking at the effects on child nutrition of the mother going out to work: the first concerns the income gains to the household, and the second is the time taken away from child-care when she goes out to work. The extent to which these changes affect the health and nutritional status of young children will depend upon a further set of intervening factors, since the economic status of the household will be

---

[27] B. Popkin, F.S. Solon, 'Income, time, the working mother and child nurtriture', *Journal of Tropical Pediatrics and Environmental Child Health*, Volume 22, pp. 156-166, 1976.

[28] C. Powell, S. Grantham McGregor, 'The ecology of nutritional status and development in young children in Kingston, Jamaica', *American Journal of Clinical Nutrition*, Volume 41, pp. 1322-1331, 1985.

significant, as will be the compatibility of the mother's employment with child-care. The quality of child-care provided by mother substitutes is also important, as are the cost, quality and availability of breast milk substitutes and weaning foods.

It is evident that certain circumstances are likely to cause a low nutritional status among children in poor households who have working mothers. First, if the mother has a job which is incompatible with child-care, early weaning onto breast milk substitutes or weaning foods might take place; and because of the danger of contamination, and the over-dilution of expensive breast milk alternatives, malnutrition is a likely result.

A striking example of malnutrition arising from the over-dilution of infants' foods is provided by Schweiger and Cutting (1978). They reported that a third of all severely malnourished infants attending a child clinic in Bangladesh in 1978 had been fed solely on powdered barley water which had been grossly over-diluted (Table 16). Furthermore, the addition of milk and sugar recommended by the manufacturer was omitted because either the parents could not afford to pay for such 'extras' or they were illiterate and thus could not read the manufacturer's instructions.

Another important reason for higher levels of malnutrition in poor families where women work is the time-intensive nature of feeding and caring for sick children. Where the mother is forced to be absent and adequate substitute care is not available, children are likely to suffer during this particularly vulnerable period.

**To sum up, it is likely to be the poverty of the household – the inability to afford adequate child-care substitutes, and the inability to afford adequate and safe food to supplement breast milk – that results in poor nutritional status, rather than the employment status of the mother as such.**

**Table 16: The protein and energy content of commercial baby food as fed to some malnourished children in Bangladesh, 1978.**

| Food for a 6 kg child | Recommended amount for 24 hours*† | Powdered milk if provided according to formula: 2 scoops × 4 in 24 hours | Barley flour as fed to some babies seen: 1 teaspoonful in 24 hours |
|---|---|---|---|
| Protein | 12 grams | 28.05 grams | 0.4 grams |
| Energy | 660 calories | 560 calories | 14.5 calories |

Note: The instructions for powdered milk usually advise the addition of sugar, and those for barley water recommend the addition of milk and sugar.
* W.E. Nelson, *Textbook of Pediatrics*
† National Academy of Sciences — National Research Council of the USA

Source: M. Schweiger, W.A.M. Cutting, 'Barley water babies — a commerciogenic condition?', *Tropical Pediatrics and Environmental Child Health*, April 1978.

### 3.3.8. Fertility and the family life-cycle

Low household income has been identified as an important determinant of low food intake, but this represents only part of the picture at the household level. Also important in understanding factors pre-disposing children to malnutrition are the point a family has reached in its life-cycle, and the relationship between its needs and its labour power or earning capacity.

Figure 4 presents a view of the life-cycle of a family, and of the relationship between its needs and resources. The household is essentially a nuclear one, consisting of a couple with four surviving children, perhaps more typical of a poor urban family than a rural one. In this imaginary family each child becomes economically active to some degree at the age of 10, and the mother resumes some economic activity when the youngest child is 2 years old. Overall food needs reach a peak as the two oldest children pass through their late teenage years, just before they leave to set up their own homes.

**Figure 4: Household food energy requirements during the period of the family life-cycle.**

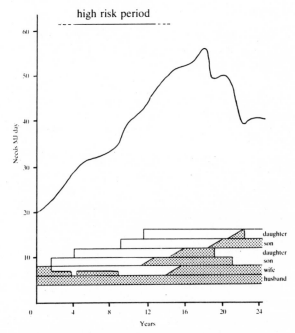

Members of household:
▨ economically active
☐ dependent

Note: The energy needs (MJ/day) of a household for 25 years after its formation (the peak value, prior to the eldest daughter leaving home, is about 56 MJ/day, or about 13,500 kcal/day).

Source: A. Pacey, P. Payne (eds.), *Agricultural Development and Nutrition*, Hutchinson, 1985.

35

During the early period of family expansion, food needs increase steeply, but without any steady source of additional labour/income. In this example, food needs increase at their steepest rate from 33 to 42 Mega Joules (about 8000 to 10,000 kilo-calories) in the two years before the oldest child begins to contribute to the family budget. **A family which copes with one or two dependent children might thus start to have difficulties when later ones arrive. Indeed, evidence from rural India has shown that the fourth and subsequent children were twice as likely to be malnourished as those born earlier.**[29] In Kingston, Jamaica, a longitudinal study of 270 infants from birth to 1 year found that children born sixth (or later) in a family were more than twice as likely to be malnourished as those born earlier.[30]

Clearly then, to identify children at risk of malnutrition we need to consider the stage reached in the family life-cycle. Other circumstances to be considered are whether the household is receiving financial or other help from members living outside the immediate family, or whether it has any commitments to support such members, either in the urban or rural areas. These characteristics vary widely in different types of towns and cities. The reader would be advised to investigate the family structure that exists locally.

Another point to consider is how recently the family has arrived in the city. Very recent migrants may find great difficulty in securing urban employment in the early days (or years) before they build up the necessary contacts to do so. Time is also required to understand and become part of the social networks that will enable them to find child-care for their infants if the mother needs to work, or to gain access to medical facilities, or to food credit systems. In short, recent migrants are likely to be disorientated and least able to avail themselves of whatever few advantages the urban area has to offer the poor.

**The intensity of the most stressful period in the life-cycle of the household will also depend on the interval between births.** The likely effect of this interval on nutrition is clearly suggested in the work of the World Fertility Survey: **on average a child born less than two years after a previous birth is twice as likely to die before its second birthday than if it had been born four years after the previous birth.**[31] Without the constraint of poverty, however, this would be less likely to be true, for in the poorest families delayed childbearing would alleviate the problem without striking at a major cause; so nutrition (and mortality) might not show so dramatic an improvement.

---

[29] C. Gopolan, 'Observation on some epidemiological factors of Protein-Calorie-Malnutrition', *Protein Calorie Malnutrition*, A. Van Muralt (ed.), New York, USA, 1969.

[30] S.M. Grantham McGregor *et al.*,'The identification of infants at risk of malnutrition in Kingston, Jamaica', *Tropical and Geographical Medicine*, Volume 29, pp. 165-171, 1977.

[31] 'World Fertility Survey - major findings and implications', *World Fertility Survey*, International Statistical Institute, Voorburg, Netherlands, 1984.

Some studies have suggested that among the poor in urban locations, birth intervals are becoming shorter than they would have been in rural life. This is attributed to reduced breast-feeding (which has occurred for reasons given above) and a consequent curtailing of its contraceptive effect. Malnutrition may occur, therefore, both in the child suffering from early weaning and in the child that follows after a short interval. The detrimental effects of two young children competing for a mother's time or milk will in part depend on the sharing practices within the household: in some societies female children may be more at risk than their brothers.

---

In this section of the analysis at the household level, we have tried to show how nutritional status is an indirect result of the ability of household resources to fulfil the basic needs of its members. Access to secure jobs, costs of food and other necessities (such as shelter), and the time-constraints of female employment in urban areas are examples of the factors to be taken into account.

---

## 3.4. Level Three: the community
### 3.4.1. Introduction

At the household level we have seen that food and nutrient intake is strongly determined by household economic status and by demographic factors such as household size and structure; whilst disease status is strongly influenced by the quality of the environment and the nutritional status of the individual.

Household economic resources and environmental quality are in turn strongly conditioned by forces that operate at the **community level**. In the urban context, the distribution of ownership and control of assets is vitally important. Who owns the land on which people live? Who has responsibility for and control over provision of sanitary and water facilities? Who controls the labour market and credit facilities for the urban poor? Who are the community leaders? What is the basis of their power and what are the objectives of their leadership? Do the objectives of the community leaders reflect those of other household groups in the community that they represent? If not, what are the implications for outside agencies and for the poorest households in the community? Each of these important questions will be discussed briefly and they will be taken up further in the case studies in Part Two of this booklet.

### 3.4.2. Poor environmental quality is a major cause of disease and malnutrition

The environmental conditions in the slums and shanty towns of Third World cities are appalling. Inadequate supplies of safe drinking water, lack of rubbish disposal and of adequate sanitary facilities lead to high risks of diarrhoeal diseases, parasites and other gastro-intestinal disorders. Over-crowding and poor housing lead to high rates of infectious diseases such as measles and whooping cough. Furthermore, the man-made conditions of the urban environment cause particular health problems for the urban poor. Industrial pollution – which is a widespread problem for all urban people – affects the poorest most severely, since a large proportion of shanty towns are situated on the periphery of a city, where manufacturing, processing and distilling plants are often built, and where environmental protection is frequently weakest. In 1984, the escape of lethal gas in Bhopal, India, which led to the death of 2,500 people, many of them squatters, dramatically demonstrated the vulnerablity of shanty town dwellers who live and work in such conditions.

The relationship between the prevalence of disease and environmental quality has been clearly demonstrated in a study conducted in 1980 in seven slums in Pune, India. The slums were selected for their variation in physical environmental quality and provision of water and sanitary facilities. In each slum area, an environmental quality index was constructed based upon the number of latrines and water taps per head, the bacterial contamination of the water and food, and an assessment of the cleanliness of the slum. A correlation was found between children reported as ill and malnourished and environmental score. Furthermore, the probability of a child being malnourished, and of a child being sick, was related to the dampness of the dwelling independently of household income.[32,33] Such evidence demonstrates the importance of environmental quality as a factor in both disease and malnutrition. Similar findings have been reported in other studies.[34,35]

Another study, conducted in 1977 in Cali, Colombia, demonstrated the relationship between child malnutrition and a neighbourhood ranking score which was based on socio-economic and environmental factors, and access to services. The 228 *barrios* or neighbourhoods in Cali were ranked and divided into seven strata with approximately equal populations in each. Household samples were randomly selected from the bottom six strata. The neighbourhood ranking scale (shown in Figure 5) is in a descending order of wealth and the quality of the environment. Neighbourhoods in the first sextile are economically better off, have better quality environments and a greater access to services than those in the sixth sextile. When the prevalence of child malnutrition was related to neighbourhood scale, distinct and significant differences were found both in deficits of weight-for-age and in deficits of height-for-age. Clearly, an interaction of economic and environmental factors is operating here to precipitate malnutrition in these children.

---

[32] M. Bapat, N. Crook, 'The environment, health and nutrition: an analysis of inter-relationships in the city of Poona', *Habitat International,* Volume 8:3/4, pp. 115-126, 1984.

[33] M. Bapat et al, *'The impact of environment and economic class on health in urban India; case studies of Pune and Durgapur'*, (mimeo), SOAS, 1989.

[34] C.G. Victora et al, 'Risk factors for malnutrition in Brazilian children; the role of social and environmental variables', *Bulletin of the World Health Organisation,* Volume 64:2, pp. 299-309, 1986.

[35] C.A. Powell, S. Grantham-McGregor, 'The ecology of nutritional status and development in young children in Kingston, Jamaica', *The American Journal of Clinical Nutrition,* Volume 41, June, pp. 1322-1331, 1985.

### 3.4.3. Who owns the slum land and property?

This is a vital question as it has implications regarding who has responsibility for the provision of basic services and housing, and for environmental quality. It also concerns security of tenure for the residents, the value of house rental and the structure of the community organisation; the latter is crucially important in terms of the feasibility and success of community development efforts, whether initiated from within or by outside agencies.

It is useful to distinguish between two basic types of slum community: legal slums, where the land and often housing is privately owned and rented out by slum landlords; and squatter settlements where the residents are illegally residing on land owned by the government, or by private individuals or companies.

---

**Figure 5: The effects of neighbourhood factors on weight-for-age in pre-school children of Cali, Colombia.**

---

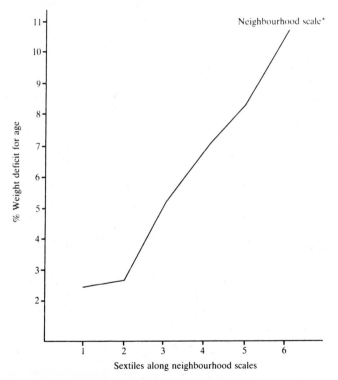

* increase is statistically significant

Source: J.S. Koopman *et al.*, 'Food, sanitation and the socio-economic determinants of child growth in Colombia', *American Journal of Public Health* Volume 71:1, January 1981.

The land in legal slums may be owned by a number of small landlords who may or may not live within the slum locality, or by large landowners – the urban elite – who usually live outside the slum locality. In general, the primary motivation of private landlords is profit. They provide land and often housing for rental and frequently have neither interest in the provision of basic services within the slum nor, if housing is rented, in the maintenance of structure. Indeed, it has often been reported that if basic services are up-graded, either by the landlord or by an external agency wishing to improve the conditions of tenants, then landlords raise the rents, displacing the poorest tenants whom the agency may have originally intended to help.

It is not unusual for the power and self-interest of these private landlords to extend beyond the control and maintenance of the physical infrastructure and collection of rent; they can exert considerable influence over their tenants and, through their ability to act as negotiators with outside agencies, create a complex dependency in the slum tenants. Such a dependence inhibits orga-nisation and consciousness on the part of the tenants; and, as has been so well reported in rural areas of many developing countries, these elite groups of landlords and their representatives may stand as nets between the poor tenants and the outside world, in the sense that they can catch and control resources and benefits.

Many large landlords are also involved in the political and civic life outside the slum and welcome the provision of 'dole out' welfare services such as curative health-care and child-feeding. Although such projects can make important contributions to the cure of acutely malnourished children and prevent the death of individuals in the short term, they are unable to tackle or improve the long-term prospects of the urban poor. Indeed, the considerable publicity which usually surrounds such projects frequently enhances the poli-tical careers of the landlord-politicians, thereby increasing further the wealth, influence and power of these elite groups.

Some landlords may also be heavily involved in illegal trading or other such activities and enjoy protection from corrupt police officers and other city officials. In these circumstances, any development project which attempts to encroach upon their territory may be perceived as a threat to business and would meet vehement opposition.

Furthermore, as owners of the slum land and property they have the power to evict their tenants and to stop development projects in their tracks.

A similar situation often exists in illegal squatter settlements. Squatters have no security of tenure and are thus under constant threat of eviction; as a consequence they have no incentive to improve their environment. Govern-ments are likely to be politically unwilling to recognise their existence or to provide basic services, and squatters may therefore be dependent upon any person or group who they perceive can give them some sort of 'protection'.

Some squatters may be used by agents – who are often powerful persons outside the squatter community – to exploit the rest of the squatters by extracting 'rent', although they do not own the land. This rent money is then shared with the so-called protectors. Their protection may go even further: they may charge fees for services to obtain titles to illegally occupied land, which never materialise. If the squatters are unable to pay, the exploiters then arrange for their forcible removal, or for them to be robbed or assaulted, or for their housing to be demolished. These outside protectors and resident exploiters often form a tightly-knit organisation which becomes a formidable force whenever there are attempts to organise squatters to fight them.

In this context, well-intentioned welfare projects such as child-feeding may unconsciously serve to increase the squatters' tolerance of the exploitative practices of these protection groups. For example, a mother who is forced to pay occupancy rent to a 'slum lord' may be unable to feed her children, and is therefore grateful that a feeding project is being implemented in her community so that her children can at least have one full meal a day; nevertheless, this feeding programme is providing the conditions for the perpetuation of slum lord activities. The conflict between short-term alleviation of distress and long-term development is clearly illustrated in examples of this kind. Such circumstances pose a real dilemma for development agencies.

### 3.4.4. Other powerful patrons of the urban poor

Private landlords and slum lords are not the only groups with whom the urban poor may be forced into relationships of dependence. Throughout this book stress has been laid on the importance of household economic status as a major determining factor in child malnourishment. In their struggle for survival, the urban poor are frequently forced into dependent relationships with a variety of potential patrons in the hope of reducing the insecurity of urban life.

The city offers a wide range of possible patrons. Among the most important are employers and 'labour lords' (who control the organisation of illegal activities such as prostitution, child labour, illegal trading and distilling, and other criminal activities) and, for the self-employed, suppliers of goods on credit. These patrons provide a minimal means of economic survival for the poor. Furthermore, they are often willing to extend loans for food, for illness or for dowries, etc. These debts may accumulate over time, intensifying further the dependent relationship. Patrons also often intercede with the police if an employee finds himself or one of his family members in minor trouble.

In return for such patronage the employee is expected to extend labour, gratitude, deference and loyalty to his employer, who is also his social superior. Work forms only part of this comprehensive dependency relationship and must be supplied when, where, of the nature (legal or illegal) and to the extent demanded by his employer.

Other important patrons for the urban poor may include: shopkeepers to whom the poor are indebted; local neighbourhood leaders; professionals and others of higher status who belong to the same home-place organisation or religious organisation; priests and other religious functionaries; and traditional leaders such as caste or clan elders or urban chieftains who are willing and able to play the role of patron.

### 3.4.5. The slum community leaders

An understanding of the social, economic and political structure of such communities and the nature of the power base of the leaders is extremely important. It will to a large extent determine the feasibility and success of united community organisation, and the effectiveness of policies and projects which are aimed at benefiting the poorest households.

Outsiders frequently believe slums and squatter communities to be homogeneous. This is rarely, if ever, the case. Such communities are nearly always extremely heterogeneous, with conflicts of interest between different economic, ethnic, kinship or religious groups.

Where exploitation by dominant factions or leaders – such as landlords, slum lords, or labour lords – is a significant force in a slum or squatter community, genuine community participation in development activities is likely to be very difficult to initiate. This is because exploitative leaders or factions, who are often recognised as 'official representatives' of their communities, are likely to be motivated in their dealings with outside agencies by the twin objectives of personal profit and/or political advancement. Such objectives are in direct conflict with the needs of the poorest household groups within the same community.

On the positive end of the spectrum, there may be enlightened community leaders or elite groups who, if mobilised, have the genuine potential to participate actively in development projects and stimulate community involvement and commitment to such projects. They might be religious leaders or elders; charismatic leaders who have gained respect in the community due to their strong personality and history of fair judgement in community affairs; trade union or labour organisers who are committed to working for change; or leaders of groups initially formed around specific interests (such as the mothers who met originally to discuss child nutritional problems in The Dominican Republic, and who progressed to become an influential force in their own communities).

A summary of the acceptability of community development initiatives to local and other elites is given in Figure 6; it is adapted from a framework devised by Robert Chambers. The difference between the acceptability to elites of short-term and long-term changes is clearly brought out in this diagram.

> **In this section of the analysis at the community level we have tried to show how the households' economic and social relations within the community, and the quality of the physical environment, all contribute indirectly to nutritional status; one cannot understand this process without first understanding the role of land and labour lords and community leaders in the political structure of a slum.**

**Figure 6: Acceptability of urban development approaches to local and other elites.**

| Dimension of urban deprivation | Examples of direct approaches | Acceptability to local and other elites |
|---|---|---|
| Physical weakness | – eye camps<br>– feeding centres<br>– family planning<br>– curative health services | High |
| Vulnerability and poverty | – employment generation<br>– interest-free (or low interest) loans: for employment, sickness, ceremonies and death<br>– upgrading housing/environment<br>– redistribution of old assets<br>– distribution of new assets | |
| Powerlessness | – legal aid<br>– enforcement of liberal laws<br>– trade union activity<br>– political mobilisation<br>– non-violent political change<br>– violent political change | Low |

Source: adapted from R. Chambers, *Rural Development – Putting the Last First*, Longmans, 1983.

## 3.5. Level Four: the national and international level

Clearly, the factors affecting nutrition that have been discussed at the lower levels in this analytical framework have inextricable links with national and international politics and policies; but to discuss all these here would be impossible. We will discuss those most affecting the urban poor.

### 3.5.1. The effect of food policies on the urban poor

The price of food to the poor is often subject to direct regulation by the government. There may be a blanket subsidy on a specific foodstuff or a rationed distribution of cheap food to those who qualify through a means test. Both schemes pertain particularly to urban areas where few people grow their own food. But not all poor people get access to such food distribution systems.

At the national level, a subsidised food policy is sometimes favoured by the owners of industry because they can pay low wages if the cost-of-living for their workers is kept down. In Egypt, for example, the wheat subsidy is said to reduce the cost-of-living by 50% for the average urban family . The ability of developing countries to maintain such policies depends on how costly the food is to produce and how large the overall subsidy therefore has to be. Budget deficits may result from subsidising food; in the early 1970s, for example, the Sri Lankan rice subsidy alone amounted to as much as one-fifth of the budgetary expenditure.

Alternatively, the necessary food is sometimes imported. The availability of cheap food imports is usually linked to the exports of grain surpluses from the West; for example, Egypt could not manage its cheap food scheme without French and American wheat being in surplus. When food is imported on concessionary terms as food aid, the financial problem of the government may be alleviated to some extent. However, the receipt of food aid can render countries vulnerable to political leverage by the donor, destroy incentives for local food production, and put the recipient in a position of long-term dependency.

The amount of breast-feeding the infant population enjoys is also partly determined by national and international pressures. The multinational corporations work through their local subsidiaries to promote commercially-produced infant foods. The WHO/UNICEF International Code of Marketing of breast milk substitutes was adopted in 1981 to control such promotion.[36] However, many governments still find it hard to withstand the power of commercial pressure. For example, in the Philippines the government brought in the Code as law in 1986; yet despite this, it has been reported that baby milk companies have found ways of circumventing the legislation.[37]

### 3.5.2. The effect of environmental policies on the urban poor

We have talked of the importance of a clean environment and adequate shelter to ward off nutrition-impairing infections. The environment may be affected by national-level politics. Many slum-upgrading programmes are devised by the central government; but unless international financial support is available, national budgetary deficits often arise out of having too many such programmes, since slum-upgrading is very costly. A possible solution to this problem is low-cost, self-help housing and environmental improvement schemes organised at the community level, thus taking the financial burden off the government; but such schemes are disliked by some national governments because they may lead to the development of local autonomy, which is seen as a threat to centralised governmental control.

Alternatively, financial support is sometimes obtained from large international agencies such as the World Bank. The object of their interventions is not always primarily to promote the health and nutritional status of the poor; for example, the opening up of slums – including the construction of a few paved roads and modest shopping precincts – may be seen by some multinational commercial organisations as a means of creating markets for Western consumer goods.

---

[36] WHO/UNICEF *'International code of marketing of breast milk substitutes'*, Geneva, World Health Organisation, 1981.
[37] BUNSO, 'Breastfeeding in the Philippines', *Health Alert*, September 1989.

### 3.5.3. The effect of employment policies on the urban poor

Finally, household income depends on employment and wage levels and both are subject to governmental policies and programmes. Some developing countries have favoured the expansion of industry in order to produce modern consumer goods such as motor cars or television sets, thus reducing the volume of imports. But such industries usually require high technology and are intensive in their use of machines and other capital inputs. Their immediate employment potential is therefore usually rather small. The majority of the slum-dwelling poor fail to gain access to this employment, and hence remain poor and at risk of malnutrition.

Other countries have gone in for promoting exports of light-weight manufactured goods which are competitive on the world market because they are cheap. But their cheapness stems from the fact that their manufacture is intensive in the use of cheap labour. The employment potential may be quite high, but wages are often low and working conditions bad for health.

Export-orientated industries also suffer from another problem: the world demand for their products may fluctuate and hence the employment of their workers is never very secure. The garments industry is a good example: the recent success of the Bangladesh industry in selling cheap clothing to Western countries soon brought opposition from the Western garment manufacturers, and restrictions on imports from Bangladesh were imposed.

Section 4.2 describes the case of Chimbote in South America, where a principal export industry – fisheries – suffered a recession. With employment taken away, the incomes and purchasing power of families are reduced; this means that they have less to spend on the goods and services of others who are employed or self-employed in the same locality. The effect snowballs as incomes decline. In the West, social security may protect families from disaster; but in the developing countries nutritional status usually declines too.

### 3.5.4. The effect of structural adjustment policies on the urban poor

In the late 1970s and the early 1980s organisations such as the International Monetary Fund and the World Bank began to impose new conditions upon developing countries to whom they were making financial loans intended to alleviate balance of payment problems and mounting debt. These conditions included the implementation of so-called structural adjustment policies. It was thought that one of the causes of the problems that these policies were designed to cure was the high levels of government expenditure on social services. Such expenditure, by raising levels of employment and incomes, led to an increased demand for imported consumer goods without a corresponding increase in exports with which to pay for them. Structural adjustment policies required the cutting back of government expenditure on health, education and food subsidies. It has been found that during this period many developing countries experienced a decline in per-capita calorie consumption. Increases in child malnutrition (for example in Ghana and Peru), or increases in the infant mortality rate (for example in Brazil) were recorded.[38] It is often difficult, however, to distinguish the effects of adjustment policies from those of the general global recession that was occurring at the same time.

In order to combat these side-effects of structural adjustment programmes the World Bank now favours the simultaneous introduction of specifically targeted nutrition programmes.[39] However, experience has shown that the strong interlinkages that exist in urban economies make such precise targeting difficult. For example in metropolitan Santiago, Chile, a feeding programme in schools was expected to alleviate the detrimental effects of structural adjustment on children in the poorest households. But between 1974 and 1983 the attendance of children in primary schools fell substantially. The worst attenders were the poorest children, whose families were most severely hit by the sharp rise in unemployment resulting from economic adjustment and contraction. In these households mothers were forced to seek employment to supplement declining family incomes, and in many cases children were sent out to beg. Hence, instead of benefiting from the feeding programme, it was reported that children in one locality of the city suffered a tripling in the incidence of malnutrition.[40] Examples such as this show the limitations of selective interventions in a programme that has come to be known as "structural adjustment with a human face".

---

**In this section of our analysis we have tried to show, using specific examples, how policies and politics at the national and international level have inextricable links with malnutrition at the community, household and individual levels; for instance through affecting the price of food, the sums spent on social services, or the employment prospects in an urban locality.**

---

[38] G.A. Cornia *et al*, (eds.), *Adjustment with a Human Face*, Volume I, Clarendon Press, Oxford, 1988.

[39] A. Berg, *Malnutrition: what can be done? Lessons from World Bank Experience*, The Johns Hopkins University Press, Baltimore and London, 1987.

[40] D. Raczynski, 'Social Policy, Poverty, and Vulnerable Groups: children in Chile', in G. A. Cornia *et al* (eds), *Adjustment with a Human Face*, Volume II, Clarendon Press, Oxford, 1988.

### 3.5.5. Summary

Figure 7 summarises the interaction of nutrition-related factors at the four social levels of analysis we have used as a framework for discussing the causes of malnutrition in the urban context. At the bottom of the diagram is shown the final outcome of the causal factors, namely the nutritional status of the child. Examples of the causal factors are grouped in boxes relating to the social level at which they operate, i.e. at the individual level, the household level, the community level, and the national or international level.

**Figure 7: A framework for the analysis of different influences on child nutritional status.**

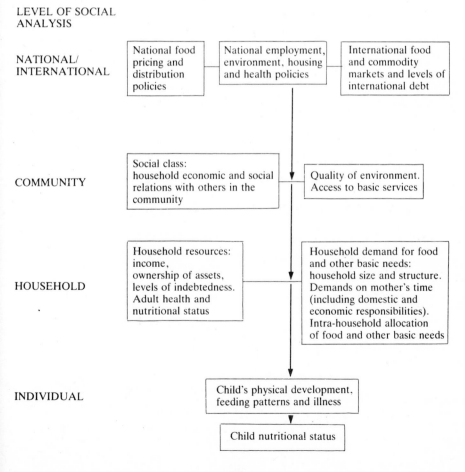

LEVEL OF SOCIAL
ANALYSIS

NATIONAL/
INTERNATIONAL

| National food pricing and distribution policies | National employment, environment, housing and health policies | International food and commodity markets and levels of international debt |

COMMUNITY

| Social class: household economic and social relations with others in the community | Quality of environment. Access to basic services |

HOUSEHOLD

| Household resources: income, ownership of assets, levels of indebtedness. Adult health and nutritional status | Household demand for food and other basic needs: household size and structure. Demands on mother's time (including domestic and economic responsibilities). Intra-household allocation of food and other basic needs |

INDIVIDUAL

Child's physical development, feeding patterns and illness

Child nutritional status

# PART TWO: CASE STUDIES OF URBAN NUTRITION INTERVENTION PROJECTS

# CHAPTER 4.

## CASE STUDIES OF INTERVENTION PROJECTS

### 4.1. Introduction to the case studies

The case studies in this part of the booklet are drawn from urban experience in the Dominican Republic, Peru, and a country in South Asia; they describe the progress of several intervention projects which tackled a wide range of issues in the course of attempting to combat urban malnutrition.

Interventions can clearly have an impact ultimately on the individual's health and nutritional status through different routes (many of which may not be traditionally thought of as 'nutritional projects'), and the focus of an intervention can be on one or more of the social levels as described in the first half of this booklet. Figure 8 illustrates this point, depicting how an employment-generating project has the potential to improve nutrition through an increase in income at the **household level**; the same project may also reduce the dependency of households on a single employer, and thus enable the **community** to be less vulnerable to the demands and conditions of work imposed by that employer. This means that employment and income security may

---

**Figure 8: Using the analytic framework to assess the potential effects of development projects on child nutrition.**

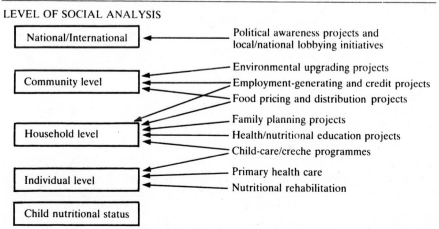

LEVEL OF SOCIAL ANALYSIS

National/International ← Political awareness projects and local/national lobbying initiatives

Community level ← Environmental upgrading projects
Employment-generating and credit projects
Food pricing and distribution projects

Household level ← Family planning projects
Health/nutritional education projects
Child-care/creche programmes

Individual level ← Primary health care
Nutritional rehabilitation

Child nutritional status

improve, and consequently the source of good nutrition in the community may be better assured.

This is an example of a project working on nutrition by focusing on problems at the household and community levels. Many projects focus on the individual directly: nutritional rehabilitation in community clinics is an obvious example. On the other hand, few projects are able to intervene at the national level; however, pressurising local authorities to provide services such as unpolluted drinking water, so that infants can be fed safely, is a legitimate activity of nutrition projects that has been adopted in several cases.

The case studies included here were chosen because they illustrate a wide variety of issues from among those discussed in the first part of the booklet. Not only do they underline the inter-relationships between disease, feeding practices, employment, environment, community politics and government policy (to name but a few of the factors) and the individual's nutritional status in the urban setting, but they illustrate ways in which intervention projects have come to recognise and tried to utilise the existence of these inter-relationships to promote the cause of improved nutrition. These projects are intrinsically interesting because of their diverse activities and their organisers' willingness to learn and progress despite the constraints they experienced. Although other illustrative projects could have been found, these three recommended themselves because of their outstanding diversity and the excellently detailed documentation over a sufficient period of time to allow for significant developments to occur.

The three projects highlight two rather different aspects of nutrition intervention. The Latin American and Caribbean case studies both describe projects which were eventually to take up issues at all the levels of intervention (as defined in Figure 7). One of these projects is distinctive in being predominantly administered and operated by women.

The focus of these case studies is on the relationships between policies at the national and international level and urban nutritional status and interventions; whereas the Asian case study describes a project that operated mainly at the individual and household levels, and the focus of the study is on the relationships between urban nutritional interventions and community politics.

The case studies differ also in the type of urban environment they describe. The Latin American and Asian case studies both concern fully built-up urban areas containing extensive slums; whereas the Caribbean case study encompasses both urban and rural areas over a semi-agricultual zone. The Latin American city is dominated by two industries, one of which is a heavy-industrial plant; whereas the economy of the Asian city is more diversified, and that of the Caribbean locality contains a large component of a single agro-industry. Between them, therefore, these case studies should cover a wide range of the experiences that project organisers are likely to face.

## 4.2. Chimbote in Peru: a city vulnerable to industrial change

### A city made vulnerable by its industries

Chimbote is both a steel-town and a fishing-town, and it was the establishment of these two industries that gave rise to the town's explosive demographic growth. From having been a mere 5,000 in the 1940s, the city's population is now (in the 1980s) around a quarter-of-a-million. Over 5,000 of the current labour force are employed directly in the giant steel mill which was set up in the 1950s, and about the same number work in the fishing industry, although in the 1960s, when fishing was at the height of its boom, it employed 10,000 people. **These two industries dominate the city: their fate decides directly or indirectly the fate of most families living there,** and with the products of both industries suffering fluctuations of fortune in world markets, the vulnerability of the population is extreme.

---

**Figure 9: Peru: Map and selected statistics.**

---

Life expectancy: 58 years
Infant mortality rate: 99 per 1000 live births
Population increase: 2.6% per annum
Population urban: 65%
Gross Domestic Product derived from industry: 35%
Per capita income: US$ 1040
Growth in Gross Domestic Product 1975–80:   1.6% per annum
                                           1980–83: −2.1% per annum
Literacy (ages 15 and over, 1972): 72%

Sources: United Nations, *Demographic Yearbook* and *Statistical Yearbook* 1983–84
         (most recent data available); World Bank, *World Bank Atlas* 1985.

Chris Steele-Perkins and Christian Aid

Water is a crucial need for good health and nutrition. But these women live in a newly-established slum built on a sand-flat just south of Chimbote, without electricity or running water. Water has to be delivered (at a price) and stored in drums, from which the women draw for their household needs.

With overproduction of steel, there was tremendous pressure to rationalise and modernise the industry in all steel-producing nations. The Peruvian Government's solution was to concentrate on the competitor mill down the coast at Pisco; as a result, at least one-third of the Chimbote mill's labour force faced the possibility of being thrown out of work (although to date such large-scale redundancies have not happened), and employment growth in this industry became a thing of the past.

The fishing industry switched from canning to fishmeal production in the 1960s, because of competition from the Japanese canning industry in the US and European markets. Then, in the mid-1970's, over-fishing of anchovies caused a crisis in the industry. In the 1980s there has been a revival in canning and fishmeal production, which is now based on sardines; but the establishment of new plants in other countries (including Chile and South Africa) poses a constant threat.

In both the steel and fish-processing industries there is uncertainty about the prospects of adequate employment and incomes tomorrow. The implications of these problems for health and nutrition among the people of the city are complex, and these are discussed below. In 1981 the Ministry of Finance estimated that about 75% of the potential work force were without sufficient work.

If massive unemployment is the eventual result of over-concentration on two once-successful industries, the dramatic success itself brought with it massive degradation of the environment. The problem was not so much the size as the **speed of growth** of the town. "There has been no urban planning. The migrant workers from the mountains set up their woven-reed shacks on any available area of desert land, and with time these land invasions have turned into the now euphemistically called *Pueblos Jovenes* (young towns), where 75% of the population live today. These shanty towns extend north and south of the small urban centre, and mostly lack the essential public services: piped water, electricity, sewage, and rubbish collection. Those who do enjoy these services suffer from frequent bursts of blocked sewage pipes, creating the famous floods of *aguas negras* (sewage waters) – a notorious health risk. At the periphery of the city, flooding from the irrigation systems of the nearby cultivated fields is common, along with plagues of mosquitoes from the stagnant waters. The city is permanently capped by a huge orange-red mushroom cloud – the smoke from the steel plant, which, because of humidity and little wind, sits over the city and slowly drifts northwards to cover the fish factories of Coishco." This graphic description by a health project worker reminds one of the conditions in other rapidly-growing areas all over the Third World.

With such fluctuations in employment and the intensely harmful environmental conditions, one would not expect the health and nutritional status of the people to be encouraging. **As many as 70% of the children seen at a clinic established by one of the health projects suffered from some degree of malnutrition.** In some of the shanty towns the infant mortality rate was recorded at 140 deaths per 1000 live births in the early 1980s (higher than the national average). The children's morbidity and mortality is dominated by diarrhoeal and respiratory infections, aggravated by malnutrition. In the population as a whole, tuberculosis is reported to be on the increase: this is a disease exacerbated by poor nutrition as well as by overcrowding. Ironically, it is thus linked to the rapid success of the industries (with consequent congestion) as well as to their disastrous set-backs (with consequent unemployment and loss of income).

The official health services are inadequate, for they have never been able to keep up with the urban growth. The public hospital in Chimbote has 25 beds for children (of whom there are 100,000). The social security hospital only caters for the medically insured (about 10% of the population). The regional hospital is one-third empty because keeping it fully staffed would be too expensive.

### Health seen as a problem of the industrial city

This introduction to the economy and the environment of Chimbote has been necessary to explain the orientation of the private health organisation known as the *Centro de Educación Familiar* (CEF), which is the major concern of this case study. Although CEF had origins in an earlier social organisation (whose emphasis was on women and the family), its formal establishment dates from 1976.

CEF (which relies on charitable donations from various overseas agencies) decided essentially to tackle two problems:

- firstly the need to rehabilitate children dying of diarrhoeal-induced dehydration (in which, as was discovered subsequently, malnutrition was frequently implicated);

- secondly to start a health education programme in the shanty towns that would emphasise the extent to which **health and nutrition were an integral part of a social problem that reflected the very reason for the existence of the city in the first place, and could only sensibly be tackled with that knowledge in mind.**

The work and method of CEF will be described, along with a more detailed discussion of how other features of Chimbote's life affect the nutritional status of its population, within the format used in the earlier half of the book.

### The individual level – rehabilitation and education

At the level of the individual child the project focused on curative treatment for dehydration, using the new tool of oral rehydration therapy. The Centre was staffed initially by one full-time and one part-time doctor and a small supporting team of nurses and teachers. By 1983 about 3,000 out-patient consultations were being achieved a year, and about 200 children were admitted as in-patients.

From the start it was intended to combine treatment with health education,

56

Training health promoters to treat the symptoms of the deprived and under-nourished urban population may only succeed in diverting energy from over-coming that poverty. The *Centro de Educación Familiar* publishes pamphlets to expose the mechanisms and results of deprivation in the city of Chimbote, so that local people can direct their efforts to removing the poverty that causes ill-health in their communities. The inscriptions on the covers say: Who are responsible? — The problem of health in Coishco (shanty town) —The people of Chimbote want to live! — Diseases of the digestive system.

and to admit at least one parent along with the child undergoing therapy as an in-patient. However, the success of this procedure was limited by two constraints. Firstly, in the current economic climate families have had to seek out every opportunity to earn money, so all adult members of the household may be working, thereby severely reducing the time available for any other continuous activity. The second constraint arose from the fact that impressing the importance of hygienic practices on parents of sick children is only easy in the cleanliness of the clinic. Even hygienic feeding practices are insufficient to protect against diarrhoeal disease if the infant is left to crawl around in an unhealthy home environment; or if there is no clean water available.

In 1981 45% of all in-patients at the clinic suffered from diarrhoeal disease and 14% from third degree malnutrition (31% second degree, 23% first degree malnutrition, using weight-for-age as an indicator).

A further difficulty encountered was that mothers who were co-admitted were very anxious about the current ill-health of their children and not, in those circumstances, very receptive to health education in general. As the project progressed, its leaders became more disenchanted with the value of their in-patient service, as it was tying down resources which they felt could be better used in individual neighbourhoods closer to the households themselves. In 1984 the clinic practice changed to treating out-patients only. It was felt that the project's educational role had to take precedence.

From the start of CEF in 1976 an educational team had been working in the shanty towns. Two workshops were established to train health promoters and midwives. Nineteen promoters were elected from four slum settlements, and ten midwives from seven settlements. Although the intention was for this team to concentrate on health education in the broad sense of helping people to understand the social causes of their ill health, in practice their training and activity tended to be too 'technical' in content. They were supported in five of the slum areas by paediatric out-patient units, but again, in practice, their resources and scope for educational rather than health service activities were severely limited.

Nevertheless, it is easy to overlook the value that fairly traditional health promotion activity may have in a poor urbanising community. **For instance, the promotion of breast-feeding is a crucial activity in a city where baby food companies have been thrusting their propaganda on a captive audience newly-arrived from the mountains**. By concentrating on the suggestion that infants who are breast-fed might be receiving insufficent milk, and by visually impressing a big healthy baby fed on formula milk on every urban mother's mind, the baby food companies succeeded in a dramatic undermining of confidence, and a consequent reduction in breast-feeding in Chimbote. To make matters worse, local doctors were often compliant and prepared to promote bottle-feeding and baby foods; even maternity clinics could be found displaying promotional advertisements.In 1984 a city-wide survey found that 50% of all babies were receiving bottle feeds by the time they were 2 weeks old. From 1979 to 1984 there was a continual reduction in the percentage of infants under 5 months old who were exclusively breast-fed.

The effect on infant health was devastatingly documented from the evidence on children admitted for acute illness to the CEF clinic in 1981. 58% of the 143 admissions had been exclusively bottle-fed, 23% of these were below 60% weight-for-age. Among the infants who were receiving at least some breast milk, only 7% were below 60% weight-for-age. In 1984, interviews with mothers showed that 40% of exclusively bottle-fed 4–6–months-old infants currently had diarrhoea, compared with only 26% of exclusively breast-fed infants of that age. It is in this context that the importance of the promotion of breast-feeding has to be seen.

At the CEF clinic mothers were encouraged to continue breast-feeding their infants during and after acute illness episodes. They were further encouraged in this practice by explanatory wall posters at the clinic. The statistical information obtained from the clinic was used in underpinning the message that the health promoters and midwives could themselves disseminate in the slum areas. Additionally, the complete story of the baby milk scandal and its ramifications was outlined in a book written by two of the CEF's volunteer staff.[41]

All this activity has been essential in order to counterbalance the effect of the powerful propaganda of the baby food companies. Indeed, in a small way such activities may be thought of as a contribution to the movement which resulted in the UNICEF/WHO codes of marketing and promotional practice in 1984. It is a form of action that can and should be replicated in all urban health projects throughout the world.

### The household: a mother's time, health and income are crucial to her children's nutrition

There could be no better illustration of the need to understand urban malnutrition in the context of the household than the experience of the families who have migrated to Chimbote. The effect of the recession in both the fish-canning and the steel industries has left many families with an unemployed adult male. At the same time, even for those fortunate enough to remain in formally contracted employment the legal minimum wage has failed to keep up with the rate of inflation (75% in 1981): it was calculated in 1981 that the average family needed 2,500 soles to meet the requirements of a minimum family diet, whereas the legal minimum wage was less than half that (1,110 soles).

One result of this state of affairs has been the necessity for many women to join the factory workforce of the canning industry on terms that deprive them of security of employment, reasonable wages, and decent working conditions.

---

[41] J. Amery, R. Lopez, *Pecho O biberon? Practicas de lactantia en Chimbote*, IPEP, Chimbote, 1984.

By relying on such casual employment the industry can cope with the increased foreign competition and the fluctuations in overseas demand. **But the compulsion to earn a family income in this way has further encouraged women to bottle-feed their babies, since the opportunity for regular breast-feeding is denied to them by this pattern of work.** Time is also too precious to allow mothers to take advantage of the programme of care for their sick children which was envisaged by the 'rooming-in' campaign undertaken in the CEF clinic. It is likely that the same constraints restricted the number of mothers able to attend health education talks planned by CEF's educational team in the slums.

In fact it might be argued that health education needs to be conducted not just within the neighbourhoods but within the gates of the factory, and CEF did indeed pursue educational work among the canning workers. It should be pointed out, however, that many women working outside their homes are not factory employees.

In addition, the mothers have suffered their own misfortunes that further restrict their time and resources to care for and feed their children. Perhaps related to the industrial depression, families have split to the extent that some 30% of mothers are abandoned by their husbands, pressurising them further to continue their factory employment for almost any wage or cost to health.

Chris Steele-Perkins and Christian Aid

**In Third World slums the increasing practise of bottle-feeding with powdered milk has been associated with worsening malnutrition and child mortality. Here is a poor people's cemetry outside Chimbote and the grave of a child who may have died this way.**

The cold, wet conditions in the fish-canning factories have undoubtedly contributed to sickness among women, leading to a reduced income with which to look after their families.

**It was an appreciation of the importance of the health of all the family members in determining the health and nutritional status of children, and the preoccupation that families have with maintaining their health, that gave rise in 1980 to an investigation into the occupational health of the workers in the canneries.** In 1985, when a new project (replacing CEF) was launched, research began into the occupational health of steel-workers. **It is one of the strengths of the independent health projects in Chimbote that they have been able to switch their attention to different problems, as the self-education of the project organisers advanced and the relative importance of particular avenues of approach was re-assessed.**

### The community

The most striking work carried out by the CEF was done by its educational team in the slum settlements. By working with other organisations (such as mothers' clubs), the team has endeavoured to **extend popular understanding of health through public talks and in discussion groups. The theme that runs through all the educational work is that health and nutritional status are primarily social, not technical-medical, issues in Chimbote.** This will have been apparent in the brief outline so far of the employment and environmental circumstances of the city.

To migrants from relatively isolated rural areas it comes as a complete innovation to think in these terms. Education along these lines can be translated into useful, health-promoting action, especially where interventions need to be implemented at a community level. The water supply, for instance, reaches most households in the slum settlements for only a few hours per day. Despite this, the authorities attempted to raise water rates by 60%. A public protest was stimulated that could hardly have occurred without the political content of the educational work in the slums. More concretely, following a thorough self-education exercise in the Coishco shanty town (where the fish-canneries are located), demands were made for improvements in the water supply: these demands were met by the construction of a reservoir. Similarly motivated demands were made for rubbish clearance services in the slums.

**From the start it had been one of the objectives of the educational work to attempt to motivate the population to articulate its needs in the form of requests to the authorities for the health services that should be provided by the State.** This part of the work never proved easy: perception of the need for collective action such as this is a step forward in understanding health as a social problem. But if independent and voluntary organisations such as CEF are looked upon by the people as the main providers of health services in the slums, the responsibility of the State is never challenged, and its duty to provide services, as new urban communities arise in the event of further migration, will go by the way.

**The most remarkable method of fostering the self-awareness of the slum dwellers was organising the taking of censuses and surveys in the slums by the people themselves.** In two cases (the settlements of La Victoria and Miraflores Bajo) the analysis and preparation of documentation arising out of the census they had taken was fully carried out by the slum dwellers, under the supervision of CEF.

The value of this exercise lies not so much in the quality of the data obtained (which may be compromised by the necessarily amateur nature of the exercise), but in the involvement of the community in seeking to understand the dimensions of their own health problems in a comparative light. For instance, establishing that the infant mortality rate in one's own community is above the national average reinforces one's sense of injustice and engenders a sense of community outrage; this goes beyond the particular distress of the individual household (which might be inclined to attribute its own misfortunes to a measure of bad luck, or to a sequence of events that gave rise to its own poverty and current environmental squalor; as if such an experience were not widely, not to say universally, shared among the slum's inhabitants). The importance of that awareness attained by the people working together is that the potential is thereby created for effective collective demands to be made, for **out of the survey undertaken by the people of the Coishco settlement emerged the articulation of a request for water which was ultimately to be met by the authorities.**

The health education team in the slums worked in co-ordination with the slum's own elected organisations. In particular, CEF was responsible for setting up Health Committees comprising delegates from each neighbourhood (defined as a group of 50 families living in neighbouring blocks). These committees assisted in the organisation of the surveys and the presentation of demands to the authorities for better health-promoting facilities.

The local organisation of the slum communities is defined in Figure 10, together with the relationship between this organisation and the Health Committees. It had always been an objective of CEF to promote the creation and development of slum health committees as an integral part of the existing popular organisations. In practice, these organisations were sometimes too weak or divided to respond adequately to this approach. However, in particular slums (such as Coishco) highly motivated and active organisations were continuing to work along the lines developed by CEF when a report was made more than two years after CEF's withdrawal from the area. Furthermore, the activities of CEF helped to some extent to strengthen the organisation of the neighbourhood committees. In that way health, as an issue seen in its broad social context, may be regarded as a catalyst for more coherent and organised community action. It was argued (again several years after the conclusion of CEF's involvement) that the Chimbote Shanty Town Federation (see Figure 10) had also been strengthened by the work it had done with CEF in representing at the city level the health-related needs of the slum populations.

## Figure 10: The local organisation of the Pueblos Jovenes.

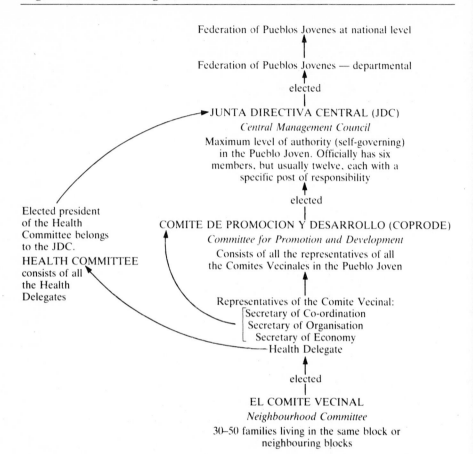

Federation of Pueblos Jovenes at national level

↑

Federation of Pueblos Jovenes — departmental

↑
elected

→ JUNTA DIRECTIVA CENTRAL (JDC)
*Central Management Council*
Maximum level of authority (self-governing)
in the Pueblo Joven. Officially has six
members, but usually twelve, each with a
specific post of responsibility

↑
elected

COMITE DE PROMOCION Y DESARROLLO (COPRODE)
*Committee for Promotion and Development*
Consists of all the representatives of all
the Comites Vecinales in the Pueblo Joven

↑

Representatives of the Comite Vecinal:
⎡ Secretary of Co-ordination
  Secretary of Organisation
⎣ Secretary of Economy
    — Health Delegate

↑
elected

EL COMITE VECINAL
*Neighbourhood Committee*
30–50 families living in the same block or
neighbouring blocks

Elected president
of the Health
Committee belongs
to the JDC.

HEALTH COMMITTEE
consists of all
the Health
Delegates

Source: Report to CIIR on the CEF project.

Among the popular organisations with which CEF also wished to co-operate were the trades unions. In practice the links were not formalised; but in at least one of the canneries quite close links were formed, until the Union was effectively suppressed. Nevertheless, the research carried out on the occupational hazards experienced by the largely female labour force is useful potential material for future groups of organised workers in the canneries to use – as they gather strength – in putting their demands before the employers. In the steel industry, on the other hand, the unions have in the past been strong, and enjoyed city-wide popular support. But it is only recently that the successor organisation to CEF has begun to investigate occupational hazards in the steel mills, with the central objective of further strengthening the Union (in the current state of industrial depression) through organisation around issues of health and safety. The potential of such initiatives is high. Time will tell how successful they can be.

In reaction to some of the earlier developments in the non-governmental sector, the Ministry of Health launched its own scheme of health promoters, often placing them in the same slums where CEF was active. On the positive side this could be seen as a reaction to the demands for health care. However, in practice the training programme, and longer-term governmental involvement in this scheme, proved quite inadequate. A CEF report stated: "These programmes reduce health care to a series of over-simplified technical skills which result in inadequate health care, but at a conveniently low cost for the Government". The insufficient supervision following the installation of these promoters allowed them gradually to succumb to a means of making a reasonable income out of their contacts with the medical business (as promoters they were expected to work as volunteers). Many became 'mini-doctors', handing out the curative drugs that the international companies dump on a society vulnerable to the magic of modern medicine and the idea of a quick fix. This is a pattern that all too easily develops as a result of the adoption of bare-foot doctors who have neither the management and motivational skills nor the economic security that would enable the replication of the programme that worked so well in China.

Karen Schofield and Oxfam

**Women gather together in Chimbote to defend the incomes they need to feed their families. High rates of inflation have eroded wages, and depression in the fishing industry has caused vessels like the one above to be laid up, and workers to be laid off.**

## National and international level

It has already been made clear how the political and economic decisions of the Peruvian Government on the question of re-siting the centre of steel production will determine the employment prospects of the people of Chimbote. We have also discussed how a capitalist enterprise such as the fish-canning business will react to the squeeze of foreign competition by tightening its grip on the working women of Chimbote. We have referred to the demoralising propaganda of the multinational baby milk producers; and to the market penetration of the multinational drug companies. These subjects have all been the topics of lectures and discussions in the CEF's educational programme: since 1981 socio-political issues have formed about 30% of the content of public education. The organisation is healthily self-critical, and public attendance at such open lectures has not been good; but when the public have been involved in the presentation of the educational material, the response and dissemination seems to have been much more encouraging.

There is clearly a lesson to be learned from the technique of communicating ideas. **In the Coishco slum the people were organised to research and present a history of their settlement, including an account of the fluctuations in the fortunes of the fisheries.** Presentation included the mounting of a photographic exhibition. There were slide shows, cartoons and leaflets. The leaflets put together information gleaned from the self-taken censuses (referred to earlier) and popularised it widely. Without this effort it is doubtful whether the inhabitants would have felt sufficiently confident of their new urban identity or their understanding of their new economic role in a larger complex system. This confidence enabled them to combine their forces, articulate their needs and marshal their arguments in the way they did when dealing with the city authorities.

## Some lessons, and some learning from mistakes

It seems that we can learn the following from CEF's experience in Chimbote. Primarily this is a project that illustrates an innovative and successful method of communication: **it involved the local people in an understanding of their health and nutrition situation by asking them to discover it for themselves.** The self-censuses and subsequent utilisation of the information gleaned to mobilise the community, and the imaginative way (in Coishco) of disseminating this information, are techniques worth copying. So are the attempts to do this by forging links with existing popular organisations, such as neighbourhood committees and trades unions. Health and nutrition can thereby be placed on the agenda for serious and well-informed political discussion and activity.

As part of this process, stress should be laid on the potential of a health project to help people to understand the wider social and economic determinants of their health and nutrition; in Chimbote, as in the Neiba Valley (see Section 4.3), this potential was utilised to the full. **In a city so heavily dependent on two industries for its survival, the opportunity to explain the links in the chain from industrial strategy to household nutrition was particularly obvious.** But the links are always there, and a society will have more

66

potential control over its future health by knowing these relationships.

Problems evolve and change, and it is necessary **to be ready to alter tactics**. In Chimbote the paediatric clinic failed as a centre of education because its conditions and environment were too far removed from the squalor of the slum, and because the demands of working time on desperately poor families prevented them from attending; hence the shift in focus to the neighbourhood and the factories. The open general meeting did not engage attention: it was not a shared experience – there were the teachers and the taught; hence the shift in focus to the didactic exhibition mounted by the people themselves, drawing on their own surveys. But there again, as the project organisers have commented, only the people who came forward to run the survey were really energised by the process: there still remained the passive majority. To communicate more pervasively with them remains the challenge of the future.

Finally, the project ran the risk of providing too **much** of a service, thereby taking the burden and responsibilities off the Government, marginalising health care to the voluntary sector, and prejudicing the future by diluting the duty of the State. Hence, when the CEF project closed in 1984, the final assessment was that the role of the voluntary organisation should be **even less one of assisting, even more one of educating,** than in the project described in this case study.

## 4.3. The Neiba Valley in the Dominican Republic: nutrition education as a catalyst for a women's movement

### Background to the Dominican Republic

It may be useful to start this case study with some background on the economy. The growth and prosperity of the Dominican Republic have been heavily dependent on its exports – predominant amongst these is sugar – and on its main trading partner, the United States. Over the 30 years prior to 1961, the sugar economy was strongly promoted by the dictator Trujillo, who bought up some of the land and mills for this purpose. On his death these fell into the hands of the State and remain Government-owned and managed to this day, while the rest have stayed in private hands.

In the early 1970s sugar accounted for 48% of exports, although some diversification had reduced this to around 35% by the end of the decade.[32] At that time the United States was purchasing two-thirds of the Republic's exports which, in addition to sugar, consist mainly of minerals, precious metals, timber and livestock. Manufacturing on the other hand is less important than the extraction of these raw materials, and the larger part of the manufacturing labour force is employed in sugar-refining. The price obtained for sugar, and therefore the value of exports and the prosperity of the Dominican workforce, has been far from stable (despite attempts at price controls made under the International Sugar Agreement from 1977 onwards).

In the light of these basic facts one has to consider the significance of the sharp social and economic inequalities that persist in the Republic. In the early 1980s 75% of the farmers owned only 15% of the arable land, and the poorest 50% of the population received only 13% of the national income. Hence the poor have very little land (or assets of any kind) to fall back on as a source of livelihood if their employment in the nation's export industries suffers as the value of exports shrinks. It was estimated in 1985 that, partly as a result of the diminished value of exports, 30% of the potential labour force was unemployed.[42]

It is also important to note that, partly because of the rapid expansion of the acreage under sugar cane over the last two decades (now about 25% of all cultivatable land), less than half the arable land in the Republic is used to grow food for domestic consumption. Of the land currently producing food, about half is used to graze beef cattle, which are also mainly exported. Clearly, exports have been promoted at the expense of growing staple food crops such as rice and corn; and it can be argued that the majority of the population in the region of the project under study have gained little or nothing from such policies.

This case study describes how the project organisers, through the initiation of a programme of self-education, confronted these and other factors which

---

[42] J.K. Black, *The Dominican Republic: Politics and Development in an Unsovereign State*, Allen and Unwin, Boston, USA, 1986.

68

contributed directly or indirectly to poverty and malnutrition in the project area itself.

## The project region of the South-West

The project lies in the South-West region bordering on Haiti, and encompassing the Neiba Valley. It is by all accounts the poorest part of the country. This was sharply demonstrated by a survey in 1969 which found that calorie intake was only 73% of the national average and that, among selected items of food, the per capita consumption of milk was only half the national average, that of fresh vegetables only one-third, and that of vegetable oil only 60% of the national average (consumption of beans and rice, the basic components of the diet, were rather closer to – though still below – the national average).[43]

Also in 1969, a nation-wide study[43] found that the children in the South-West region of the country had the highest levels of malnutrition. One-third of the children suffered from second and third degree malnutrition, which was 5-7% higher than in other parts of the Republic, and in 1976 it was recorded that the Infant Mortality Rate was around 115 per 1000 live births in parts of the area,[44] substantially above the national average. Illiteracy is also widespread here, especially amongst women: a survey in the region indicated female literacy levels to be around 30%.[44] Clearly, our project area is particularly deprived; some of the economic reasons for this are outlined below.

The South-West rural economy is strongly dominated by sugar, with the plantations taking up 40% of the arable lands. The rest is farmed mainly on a sharecropping basis, and there are very many smallholders, who can be considered subsistence farmers although their plots are hardly large enough for their survival. In addition to sugar, cotton and coffee, which are exported from the region, the project documented that 90% of the cattle produced in the South-West were exported, as was 80% of the fish, 92% of the bananas and 80% of the grapefruit and kidney beans. The region is also a source of mineral deposits extracted for exports.

The sugar estates in this area (which are entirely owned by the State) harbour the worst poverty. The labourers employed on these estates (known as *batayes*) are mainly illegal Haiti immigrants; as a result of their illegal status their wages are kept low, and they can be deported if they attempt to protest or organise. The housing conditions on the *batayes* are grossly inadequate, with barrack-like buildings allowing a single room per family, with other facilities shared. There is a shortage of water, latrines and medical care. As a result of all these factors, levels of child malnutrition in the *batayes* have been recorded as the worst in the region.

---

[43] W.H. Sebrell, 'Nutritional status of middle and low income groups in the Dominican Republic', *Archivos Latino Americanos de Nutricion*, Volume XXII, July, Special Number, 1972.

[44] These figures are based on surveys conducted under the project and reported in internal project documents.

The only manufacturing industries in the region relate to agriculture and employ a mere 13% of the workforce. The predominant source of industrial employment is sugar-refining, the major mills being located in the port-town of Barahona (on the south coast) (see Figure 11). This town is of a moderate size, with 78,000 inhabitants (many of whom are migrants from the rural areas of the region) who are engaged in a variety of service and trading activities connected with the sugar-refinery and the docks. Barahona has a settlement area interspersed with poor-quality housing (the locality of the *barrios*, known as the *Pueblos Nuevos*) where the project has its headquarters. Some

**Figure 11: Dominican Republic: Map and selected statistics.**

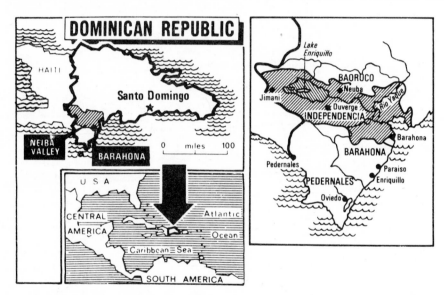

Source: D. Morley *et al.*, *Practising Health for All*, Oxford University Press, Oxford, 1983.

Life expectancy: 62 years
Infant mortality rate: 64 per 1000 live births
Population increase: 2.5% per annum
Population urban: 52%
Gross Domestic Product derived from industry: 22%
Per capita income: US$ 1380
Growth in Gross Domestic Product 1975–80: 4.5% per annum
                                   1980–82: 2.8% per annum
Literacy (ages 15 and over, 1970): 67%

Sources: United Nations, *Demographic Yearbook* and *Statistical Yearbook* 1983–84 (most recent data available); World Bank, *World Bank Atlas* 1985.

of the migrants are single women and wives who have been left to fend for themselves and their children while their menfolk search for jobs in the more prosperous parts of the country. Poverty has forced many of these women to seek jobs as domestic servants, traders or factory labour (receiving even lower wages than the men) or, in the final resort, as prostitutes. But 80% of the women in this poverty-stricken region are unable to find paid employment outside the home.[45]

This is an area that has become commercialised and the settlements have developed in response to this process. However, the population density of those settlements is not on the whole as intense as in Chimbote (Section 4.2) or Kalipur (Section 4.4); here there is at least some marginal (although somewhat saline) land bordering or interspersed among the settlements. The project extended its operations throughout the peri-urban *barrios*, the sugar estate townships and the rural villages: hence it is not an urban project in the · sense of focusing solely on the problems of intra-city slums.

### A questionable nutrition intervention

In 1969 WHO were invited to undertake a nutrition survey throughout the Dominican Republic. 75% of the children under 5 were found to be malnourished, and the incidence of severe malnutrition and infant mortality were found to be highest in the South-West of the country; so the area was given the highest priority in a major programme of nutrition interventions which was established in 1974. It was administered by the official agency of the Roman Catholic Church in the Republic (CARITAS Dominica), supported by the Catholic Relief Services and financed by the United States. The aims were "to lower Infant Mortality Rates" and "to improve dietary habits, child-care and sanitation".

The main feature of the programme was the establishment of feeding centres where mothers and children received meals prepared mostly from foreign food aid: wheat, corn and soya. The centres had no money for buying local staple foods such as rice, beans and plantains. Some of the mothers tended to regard this food aid (which was of a kind largely unfamiliar to Dominicans) as a 'wonder food', although others, for similar reasons, fed it to their animals in disgust. It was meant as a supplement, but those who used it regarded it as a substitute; hence it was eaten as the main meal of the day. It was shown later, as a result of weighing the children in various communities over a period of two years, that malnutrition persisted. More specifically, it was found that the children actually gained weight during the month when food aid was **not** distributed.

The irony was that, because the 'wonder food' had been used as a substitute instead of a supplement, it had actually contributed to malnutrition In practice, so long as sufficient food was available, the mothers were quite

---

[45] These figures are based on surveys conducted under the project and reported in internal project documents.

capable of providing a nutritious diet for their children. Their basic knowledge was not lacking, but they knew rather less about the nutritional properties of the foreign food and, clearly, there were no adequate attempts to educate them on this score. So they used it as a substitute for, instead of a supplement to, the main diet. When food was short it did not help them to be trained in the use of foreign foods which could only be provided cheaply so long as the Republic's trading partners had large food surpluses to dispose of. In fact **it could be positively undesirable to inculcate tastes for foreign foods which would normally be too expensive for the poor.**

At the same time, the free distribution of food was regarded as humiliating. The system, which involved queueing up at the distribution points, was not entirely welcomed by the beneficiaries. What was worse, it enhanced the division of power in an already divided society: rationing the gifted food supply became another source of local political patronage. (The importance of such patronage in the allocation of urban jobs and tenancies among the poor has been discussed in earlier sections of this booklet.) It is evident that food aid may well contribute to the humiliation already suffered by the poor.


**An alternative approach**

At the same time the CARITAS programme had embarked on some nutritional research involving local people, who formed the nucleus of a new development. By the end of 1976 the agency had set up a Centre for Nutrition Education and Recuperation (CERN) in a poor locality of Barahona. The Centre was planned and supervised by a nutritionist from London, and its purpose was four-fold:

– to recuperate severely malnourished children, using mainly local foods;

– to undertake projects to increase family incomes;

– to undertake projects to help to finance the organisation itself;

– to undertake nutrition education in the broadest sense.

Initially there was a sceptical reception for such a project among the local women and ambivalence among the interventionists themselves. "A nutritionist....... telling us how to cook our food? Who knows better than we about rice and beans?" "On the other hand, the malnutrition is there.....children dying.....from malnutrition, babies over and over again suffering from diarrhoea and vomiting," are words that summarise the problem as seen by the nutritionist. The latter was convinced that some knowledge **was** lacking which could help towards better nutrition in the current situation of poverty and high food prices.

It took time and patience before it was possible to start something concrete; during that time the important thing was to become friends and neighbours, simply to chat about personal life, the children's health, to talk about cooking, to be asked about buying. Then after several months came the first activity: weighing the children. The women agreed to it out of curiosity; for the nutritionist it provided a crucial benchmark. The result was the first spontaneous and serious involvement of local mothers in the project. About 50 women from the communities agreed to attend the first twelve-month course (regardless of their husbands' opposition), leaving the families for three days in each month. "The course was based on nutrition, but not exclusively," writes their nutritionist; **nutrition was the link, a starting point to reach all aspects of their lives: socially, economically, politically.**

These women became responsible for organising programmes of health education in their various communities in and around Barahona in the South-West. They were called the *promotoras*, and became the backbone of the project.

In 1977 a second CERN was established. Severely malnourished children were treated as before, but only on condition that their mothers agreed to attend the centre for half-a-day a week while the children were recovering; for nutritional support without nutritional understanding was considered useless.

It was becoming clear to the *promotoras* that the food they were distributing at the CERNs, and which came from the United States, was not an appropriate form of aid. It was costly to transport and store, and the money the Government contributed for this purpose could instead be allocated to projects of local food production, reafforestation, or increased water supplies for the communities and their fields. Instead of food aid, monetary aid could be used on local projects to prevent poor nutrition of the people from occurring in the first place. But the donors, to whom the project appealed because of food surpluses, refused. This in itself was a political education, and was a major turning point in the development of the programme. **The women decided: they themselves would fight for changes towards a real and better life. Help from outside, which was sorely needed, would only be asked for and accepted if it would support self-development.** Fortunately, such alternative help was forthcoming.

### The project

It can be seen from the four-fold purpose of the project that there were two major types of activity taking place in the communities themselves. Firstly there was the **nutrition education**. And secondly there were the income-generating or **economic projects**.

### Educational methods

At the core of the educational process were the fortnightly discussion groups of the local women, held by the *promotoras* in each community on themes that had been worked out in advance by their supervisors. The method adopted was to take a theme – such as the shortage of water and its nutritional implications – and to encourage the women themselves to express what they understood about the importance of water and why they had so little access to it. By asking themselves and each other about these questions they began to

73

formulate **by themselves** an understanding of the nutritional and economic relationships that they had not explicitly grasped before.

They were aware, for instance, that water was plentiful in that sugar cane has an enormous thirst, and yet was thriving in the South-West where they lived; their personal problem of shortage must therefore relate to how the water was allocated. This raised in their minds the question of who owned the sugar plantations and the importance of sugar to the export-orientated economy. By searching out answers from discussions within the groups, the local women began to clarify the link between malnutrition and water-related disease in their families, and the dependence of the Republic's economy on sugar exports. This self-educating process was first expounded as a methodology by the famous educationalist Paulo Freire. His teachings became a model for the educational process in this project.

An understanding of the links between the social, economic and political facets of the womens' lives and their children's nutritional status had started with the analysis of the first community nutrition surveys the women carried out. They themselves had had to confront the puzzle that the nutritional status of their children seemed to improve during the avocado harvest, when food aid was least utilised. And they themselves had discovered the solution:

Sam Clarke and Oxfam

**Women together in the south-west of the Dominican Republic enquire into the social as well as the technical causes of malnutrition in their families. Out of these discussions a song will often emerge pointing out the injustices in their society. Above a recording session is being held by** *Promoción de la Mujer del Sur.*

that the food aid was being used as a substitute rather than to supplement the basic diet.

Other themes taken up for discussion over the years have included the importance of breast-feeding, the problem of insufficient schools, the position of women in their society, the populist appeals made by politicians in the general election (of 1986), and even the implications of finding oil at some future date in the region of the South-West.

Sometimes the discussion groups have taken a document for study, such as the United Nations Human Rights Charter in relation to the Rights of the Child, or a pamphlet put out by the Dominican Centre of Legal Aid and Research entitled 'Do You Know Your Rights?', based on nutrition and health. After studying these documents the women compared, item by item, their own and their children's situation with the norms laid down in the various documents (but which are only enjoyed by the more affluent families in the more prosperous regions of the Republic).

An important item at each discussion group is a model menu, with a balanced nutritional content but using only local foods. One menu, for example, consisted of a soup containing all the daily nutrient requirements. However, the women themselves were sometimes critical of the practicality of suggestions put forward in the discussion groups: a recipe for a weaning food consisting of a puree of kidney beans, for instance, proved to be too costly in the fuel required for cooking.

Out of these discussions a song would often emerge, pointing out the injustices in their society. Or a small drama would be acted out to emphasise a social theme – the conflict, for example, between the 'expert's solution' and the 'situation in the field'. The songs and socio-drama were clearly motivational and had a broad appeal. They helped to consolidate serious social and economic matters in the minds of women, who had never been encouraged to think beyond the constraints of the household. Hence these matters became topics of everyday conversation and thought.

The women also illustrated some of the discussion themes with large murals – collages put together from newspaper illustrations and headlines. As with the songs and dramas, this is another way in which the problem of illiteracy can easily be overcome.

Perhaps the most successful way of communicating ideas to large numbers of people in the Neiba Valley was the local radio station, known as Radio Enriquillo. This was a community radio station set up with the purpose of serving the needs of local organisations and projects like this one. A regular time-slot was allotted to a programme for women, using themes from the project: some of the socio-dramas have been recorded and broadcast, and also model menus-of-the-month. Other more general programmes included contributions from the women in the project. About 25% of the settlements in the valley were able to receive the broadcasts, and radios are reported to be widespread among the poor within these settlements, so that any message would reach a substantial number of households by this means (whereas in a community as deprived as that described in the Kalipur case study [Section 4.4], access to radio would be too limited for this method of communication to have any value whatsoever).

The sense of solidarity that is promoted by hearing colleagues in one's own organisation broadcasting over the radio was furthered in another way. The project bought a bus which was used to take the women in one local group to meet the women of another distant group; common problems and solutions could be discussed and a sense of communal strength engendered. The bus was also used to take groups to other parts of the country to show the economic contrasts, the evidence of the wealthier classes and of more prosperous locations – such as the capital city – which, the women were to argue (in later discussions), drained resources and industrial profits away from the region of the South-West. These bus excursions had yet another benefit: by taking women away from their homes for two or three days at a time, they forced the men of the households to undertake domestic chores (work usually considered by the men to be unproductive, and hitherto taken for granted).

For those who were more literate the project produced its own magazine, illustrated with bold drawings to bring out a theme of topical interest or discussion. For example, they devoted one issue of the magazine to the problem of their limited access to, the high cost and the poor quality of water. The water quality was tested for bacterial contamination and the magazine illustrated their findings with a graphic sketch of a technician peering down a microscope at the bacteria abounding in a water droplet (see Figure 12). Another illustration in the same issue showed the uses of water and its vital role in the maintenance of good nutrition: for cooking, for watering vegetables and for keeping the environment clean. The women also contributed to other newsletters, and cartoons pointing out social injustices were incorporated into a local newspaper which circulated in the urban *barrios*.

**Perhaps it can be seen from these examples how nutrition education and the fostering of control over one's own and one's family's nutritional status were being used by the organisation as catalysts towards the struggle for basic human rights.**

### Economic projects

When the organisation decided to give up the use of food aid in the late 1970s it sought support from charitable organisations overseas, as the project organisers realised that switching from total dependency on foreign funds to total financial self-sufficiency was impossible. Fortunately, CARITAS in Holland (and other European organisations) came to its aid. They agreed to supply free powdered milk, which was distributed in a sensible way to avoid the hazards of the insanitary environment: it was made up in advance with boiled water, if the local water was found to be impure, and sold at much less than the market price through 'milk posts'. The scheme paid its way and indeed made a 12% profit which was invested in other activities. By 1980, there were 40 milk posts throughout the project area, and the milk was also provided at the CERNs.

It might be argued that continued reliance on foreign-supplied food was undesirable, and that there was a risk that it might be used as a substitute for breast-feeding. But at least the product was familiar to the Dominicans, and the manner in which it was distributed to avoid contamination was intelligent; and given the severity of the nutritional crisis, supplementation of one kind or another appeared at the time to be crucial. It was hoped that it could be phased out in time.

---

**Figure 12: Learning to take action on drinking water.**

---

WATER CONTAMINATION

THE WATER OUR PEOPLE DRINK IS NOT FIT FOR HUMAN CONSUMPTION.

EVIDENCE OF THIS IS PROVIDED BY THE INDEPENDENT UNIVERSITY OF SANTO DOMINGO.

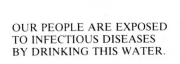

OUR PEOPLE ARE EXPOSED TO INFECTIOUS DISEASES BY DRINKING THIS WATER.

Source: Newsletter published by PROMUS.

Another scheme was the setting up of retail food shops selling only nutritious national foods (and no luxury items), with proper quality control and fair trading, fixing the prices to ensure no more than a 10% profit margin. One important side-effect of this was to force the local retailers to be more honest and to cut their monopoly profits so as to be able to compete. One of the shops was able to invest its profits in a pre-school centre. It was intended that these shops should serve as models which the Government could imitate: in practice such imitations have so far proved unsuccessful.

Food stalls were also started, selling such things as bean soup and rice, yucca leaf soup, milk, fruit juices and fresh fruit. They performed the useful function of making some of the model recipes-of-the-month affordable to the poorest families. For example, the bean soup was produced at the food stalls in large quantities with the aid of a liquidiser, so it could be sold at a price which was lower than the cost of cooking it at home. Indeed, fuel costs are so high in the Republic that some found it cheaper to eat at the food stalls on a regular basis; as a consequence they became popular meeting places.

Two major areas that the economic projects sought to cover were animal and vegetable farming on marginal land, both within Barahona and in the rural areas. The largest undertaking was chicken-farming, which aimed to sell chicken meat cheaply, thus increasing local consumption and providing additional employment and income. Eventually about eight farms were in operation. They were each managed by small teams of about five to seven women, some of whom had attended a chicken-rearing course run by the Ministry of Agriculture. Each farm had several thousand chickens. This scheme was run as a self-contained undertaking, with its own bank account.

Some problems were encountered in the operation of the scheme, and it is useful to reflect here on the difficulties frequently reported about economic projects of this kind which may be attached to nutritional intervention projects in order to raise money or supplement diets. Firstly, a common criticism is that such projects are sometimes, despite good intentions, too ambitious; from the beginning they are too large-scale and their pace of expansion is forced. A second problem emerges in the need to provide good technical back-up and training for the managers, for the scheme will require skills and experience which they do not yet have.

The chicken farms were certainly on a large scale, and used materials and equipment in their construction and operation that were unfamiliar to the participants. Also, in this case the centralising of finances proved difficult for the individual farm managers, who needed more independent control over their operations. Finally, two external factors brought the scheme to an end: first a hurricane, which made it impossible to obtain chicken-feed or replacement chicks; and second the Government, which set up farms in direct competition and with much better technical and financial assistance (which they had refused to give to the women's groups).

Somewhat similar problems arose with breeding rabbits and a pig-fattening scheme. In both projects the animals sickened and died. A scheme for cattle-farming was never started – perhaps wisely, in view of the problems encountered in the chicken-farming projects – although the women's groups strongly favoured an early end to their dependence on the imported milk powder, and this would have been a solution if successfully managed. A further scheme for substituting locally-produced soya milk also failed to progress beyond the experimental stage. What these schemes demonstrated, however, was the boundless energy of the women in seeking solutions and innovations to forward the independence and prosperity of the organisation.

The vegetable gardens project was one of the more successful schemes; it aimed to increase family consumption of vegetables and to promote the acquisition of skills in cultivation and marketing. But here too there were problems, although this time mainly social, not technical. The need to rent land was a permanent deterrent, and inadequate access to water was always an inhibiting factor. However, **the value of operating economic projects as part of the educative process is illustrated by the problem of the water shortage.** Stimulated by the practical difficulties encountered, discussion groups investigated the real issue behind the shortage of water: the fact that most of the available water went to the sugar plantations. Vegetables also require a regular water supply, but they are not grown by the powerful and the rich, so they are permitted to wilt. The women pointed out that the Government was able to construct major road- and water-works benefiting the rest of the island, but would not lend the resources necessary to tap the water not far below the surface in the Neiba Valley for the benefit of the poor, small farmers who lived there.

In 1980 the managers of the economic projects undertook a self-evaluation. They were conscious of the educative value of the projects; but they also felt that it was important to avoid attracting people to take on the job of *promotora* in the hope of making money from being involved in the management of a profitable project. It was decided that in future the *promotoras* should not be allowed to have an economic interest in the organisation.

Clearly, not all of these schemes could be copied in more densely built-up urban areas. But there are many urban or peri-urban settlements where marginal land can be exploited for such undertakings. Many city slums have at least some communal land within them where hogs and chickens roam, and where schemes such as those described here would be feasible.

### The organisation of the project

Now that the main activities of the project have been described, the organisational structure, as it stood in 1979, can be outlined without difficulty. The backbone of the organisation consisted of the 80 or so women's groups, each having about 30 members (making a total of some 2,500 women). Such a comprehensive and widespread project as this one needed a coherent administrative structure, and it is to the credit of the women's organisation that this was achieved.

79

Each group was supported by a *promotora*, who received a small remuneration. The region was divided up into five zones (one of which was the area covered by the sugar plantations, the *batayes*, and another by the urban *barrios*) and a full-time supervisor plus assistant was in charge of each zone. They would oversee the management of the economic projects and co-ordinate the topics for discussion in each zone.

At the apex of the organisation was the co-ordinating body which included the zonal supervisors and their assistants, three members who supervised the pre-school centres, one member in charge of action-research activities, and the consultant nutritionist from Europe. The latter was a remarkably energetic person and a valuable stimulus to the organisation; but it is important to note that the strength of the organisation and the responsible involvement of the local women were sufficiently established for the momentum to be maintained after her departure from the project. The fact that the women came from the communities themselves (for instance, one of the *promotoras* in the Haitian zone was herself born of Haitian parents) was significant in sustaining unity and rapport.

One of the changes that followed the 1980 re-assessment and self-evaluation was aimed at further democratisation of the organisation. The body at the apex, known as the Council of Management, was to consist of members drawn from teams involved in the specific activities in the field. These teams were named after the activities they addressed: the economic projects team, the nursery schools team, the education team, etc. (see Figure 13).

**Figure 13: Administrative structure of Promocion de la Mujer del sur, Inc., 1981.**

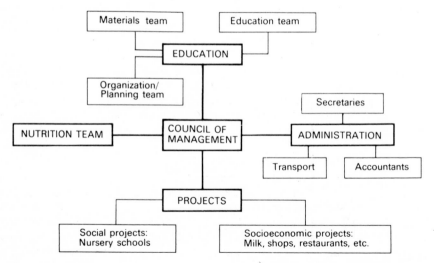

Source: D. Morley *et al.*, *Practising Health for All*, Oxford University Press, Oxford, 1983.

## The evolution of a women's movement

There is evidence that the CERNs were reducing malnutrition – or at least preventing its recurrence. About 150 severely malnourished children treated on the scheme were followed up over four years: neither the original children nor their siblings suffered malnutrition. By 1978 the immediate battle had largely been won: the original CERNs started to close, happily for lack of custom, and two of them were converted to nurseries (see Figure 14).

**Figure 14: Nutritional status of children under 5 in project area, 1974–78.**

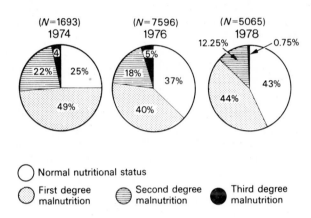

Source: D. Morley *et al.*, cited in Figure 13.

In 1979 (the Year of the Child), something occurred that pushed the project further on the road to becoming a social movement. A hurricane devastated the island, the worst cyclone of the century; and within a year, two further cyclones inflicted damage on the South of the Republic. The privation was not equal for all Dominicans. As the nutritionist put it, "The cyclones taught the women – and others – not only that nature can tear down the precious results of hard work, but especially that cyclones mainly destroy the poor and the weak. Good buildings resist.....rich groups have ways to restore water supplies.....but not the poor." This realisation was to be consolidated by the manner of the administration of food relief which poured in from outside.

When the people of the Neiba Valley found that the emergency food was not reaching them, the women took a stand. They requested the donor agencies to deliver the food via their own port in Barahona and not through the national capital of Santo Domingo, and they guarded the docks of Barahona to prevent pilferage. However, pilfering was so firmly entrenched in society that the dockers refused to unload with the women present, whereupon the women began to unload the ships themselves.

This sequence of events marked a high point in the social awareness and assertiveness of the participants in what began as a nutritional intervention programme. It was followed by an open letter signed by 1700 women and published in six daily papers, drawing attention to the sham that the Year of the Child had, in their view, turned out to be: health services remained inadequate, schools were poor, child labour persisted, and food got diverted away from the most needy.

It had now become apparent that, like it or not, the women's nutritional project had to become a social movement. To facilitate the realisation of this need, the organisation – which had already begun to call itself *Promoción de la Mujer del Sur* (The Advancement of Women of the South), PROMUS for short – sought to become a registered constitutional body. In 1982, this was finally achieved.

### Campaigning activities of the movement and its progress towards maturity

While PROMUS was securing this considerable achievement, the economy of the Dominican Republic was heading towards a crisis. The sugar production was no longer so valuable. There was too much on the world market in the 1980s. Its price dropped. The United States cut the amount it would take from the Dominican Republic. The country began to run into serious debt, and the Government had to increase the money supply in order to keep up its expenditure on public services and developmental activities. Prices rose – but the incomes of the labourers, many of whom were directly or indirectly working on sugar production, did not increase.

The women collected and discussed these statistics. By 1985, the sad spectre of malnutrition had returned, after many years' absence that had been due in part to the achievements of PROMUS. In that year the topic of discussion among the groups returned to the theme that had been current after the hurricane: why does this crisis, which is beyond our control, hit us, the poor, more than the rich? Again this was a clear example of how closely malnutrition can be linked to international trade and its fortunes.

The International Monetary Fund came 'to the rescue' of the ailing economy. But in return for financial aid the Fund imposed conditions: the Government had to reduce its expenditure and raise the prices of its services so as to cover its costs and avoid subsidies. Now among the services provided from government funds is the water supply. The Government increased the water charges and cut back on expenditure, leading to an irregular, contaminated water supply.

The women's movement responded by mounting a campaign for the non-payment of water bills. In every village and *barrio* the women co-ordinated the campaign, collecting unpaid bills, encouraging people to withhold payment and organising protest marches. In a number of townships the women commissioned independent analyses of drinking water and then publicised the results (see Figure 12). The Government retaliated. The water supply was cut off from those who refused to pay their bills. The women's movement was acquiring a degree of maturity however. They contacted the unions whose members were employed in the water service, and the unions agreed to facilitate the restoration of the water supply.

It is an outstanding example of the development of confidence in the most unlikely circumstances that women, who had hesitated to leave their homes and come to classes if their husbands were unwilling to let them, had attained the awareness and audacity to pursue their grievances in the way they did. They had perceived that there was something which could be done within the control of the people. They could not change the price of sugar, or boycott the IMF. But they could challenge their Government as mediator between the international world and their community's distress on a specific and pertinent issue. As one commentator noted, "**This project shows the *process* of growing awareness and building social organisation, but it also exemplifies how understanding comes through action; the two reinforce each other and develop side-by-side**".

The outcome of campaigning has not only been effective in raising the level of public awareness, but it has also been directly constructive in gaining some material benefits. In one of the *barrios* in Barahona a well was dug and electricity supplies were provided as a result of representations by PROMUS to the local municipal authorities. It should also be emphasised that an important reason for PROMUS's success in its activities is that it is not operating in isolation. In addition to its pragmatic alliance with a local trade union, it has supported peasant organisations, offering the practical guidance of its members in helping the organisations carry out their aims. The local radio has been crucial in forging links and creating understanding between the various organisations in the Neiba Valley that participate in its programmes.

### The strengths and importance of the project

As a postscript to this story it is worth reflecting that although a nutritional intervention project grew into a social movement, it was never affiliated to a political party, and so it retained true support from, and indeed remained composed of, ordinary people who might otherwise have been alienated. At the same time it could maintain a dialogue with, and receive aid from, bodies (internal and overseas) that would have been unable to support an organisation promoted by a political party.

A second major strength of PROMUS as an organisation was **its ability to engender leadership and involvement from within its membership:** it owed its strength and continuity to the energy and commitment of many of the *promotoras*.

A third major strength lies in **its willingness and ability to engage the mutually supportive co-operation of other movements and institutions:** in that way it became a force to be reckoned with.

The exceptional interest of the project lies in two of its characteristics. Firstly of note is the way in which, in a country where women's status was particularly low, a nutritional organisation could evolve into a women's movement, supervised and operated entirely by women, and addressing issues and using methods that would have been regarded in this, as in many societies, as well outside the women's domain. Secondly, it is impressive to see the way a nutritional organisation was able to tackle issues (such as the poor water supply) that were crucial to nutritional health, but might not normally be thought of as part of a nutrition project. These issues were selected carefully as being those which could be controlled or influenced by the organisation. Crucially, however, the pace of these developments was never forced, and the bounds of acceptable campaigning activity were not overstepped. In a different situation, other issues – such as questions of house rent, or fuel prices, or local employment – might be more appropriate.

At the same time, the organisation pursued more conventional but wide-ranging activities to promote nutritional health, day-by-day, year-by-year. There were the vegetable gardens and poultry projects to provide food and female employment. There were the highly successful educational meetings each month, discussing both the social causes of malnutrition and ways to cope with limited food resources by attempting new recipes. There was the invaluable engagement of the local radio station to broadcast ideas on social issues and nutritional advice. There was the use of a local community newspaper to popularise ideas on links between food and society. There was the supplementary supply of milk through the milk posts at prices the poor could afford.

While it is true that not all these activities could be copied elsewhere, especially in more densely built-up urban slum areas, nevertheless with local variations many of the schemes could be taken up in peri-urban areas. Most important of all, the educational and organisational methods, ideas and activities could be adopted (again with local variations) in many towns and cities throughout the developing world.

## 4.4. Kalipur in Asia: slum politics and nutrition interventions

### Kalipur: city of refuge

Kalipur (pseudonym) is a city in South Asia, covering an area of around 25 square miles and having a population of approximately 750,000. Kalipur, in contrast to Chimbote, has a modest and diversified industrial base and is well-connected by rail and road to a major port. Historically Kalipur has been an important regional trading centre, partly due to its close proximity to a major city and to its port.

The city is growing rapidly, and this growth is expected to continue: the estimated population in the year 2000, with a moderate growth rate, is around 2 million. Apart from natural increase, **the impetus behind this growth has been industrialisation, and large influxes of migrants who come from the surrounding rural areas in significant and increasing numbers as a result of continuing rural pauperisation.** Currently, more than 50% of the rural households in the region are effectively landless (i.e. cultivating less than 0.5 acres of land).

---

**Figure 15: Selected statistics for the country in South Asia.**

---

Life expectancy: 48 years
Infant mortality rate: 133 per 1000 live births
Population increase: 2.7% per annum
Population urban: 15%
Gross Domestic Product derived from industry: 10%
Per capita income: US$ 130
Growth in Gross Domestic Product 1975–80: 4.3% per annum
                                                 1980–83: 2.7% per annum
Literacy (ages 15 and over, 1974): 26%

Sources: United Nations, *Demographic Yearbook* and *Statistical Yearbook* 1983–84 (most recent data available); World Bank, *World Bank Atlas* 1985.

---

Such masses of migrants have led to the mushroom-growth of slums: some illegal, established by squatting, others legal, constructed on privately-owned land where tenants pay rent to slum property landlords. The slum population of Kalipur city is officially estimated to be about 38% of the total population of the city, although figures in the region of 50–60% are likely to be more realistic because of the difficulties of counting the urban poor: in addition to the large, easily identifiable slum areas, there are many small slum settlements throughout the city.

Government health facilities in the city are very limited. There is a 150–bed general hospital, a 100–bed TB hospital, a 20–bed infectious diseases hospital, 3 urban dispensaries, 1 school health clinic, 1 TB clinic, 14 family planning clinics and 6 sterilisation centres. These are widely scattered, and are socially and economically inaccessible to the urban poor, who complain that they do not get adequate attention or sufficient medicines from these establishments.

There are several privately-owned mother-and-child health clinics and maternity centres, but these are only attended by the middle and upper classes because the services provided are too expensive for the poor. The Kalipur children's hospital – a private charitable institution set up by a group of enlightened local doctors – has failed to function effectively due to insufficient funding, because it is totally dependent on irregular and inadequate donations from local elites and support from the Government. The poor are thus forced to resort to the drug stores manned by unqualified traders whose main motive is profit, to quack doctors, and to a whole host of indigenous practitioners such as spiritual and religious healers and homeopaths.

**Health and nutrition intervention : from disaster relief to the provision of services for slum communities**

URBAID (pseudonym), a non-governmental organisation, originally came to Kalipur in the early 1970s. Initially URBAID was involved in a relief operation in the region and ran a series of mother-and-child health (MCH) clinics and child-feeding centres in the rural and urban areas of Kalipur district. In the lat3 1970s most of these centres were closed down or handed over to the Government, leaving one busy MCH clinic and one child-feeding centre in the heart of Kalipur city itself. These two centres are still in operation today. The MCH clinic, which serves the whole of Kalipur city, provides curative treatment and immunisation for children under 5 years old; and ante-natal and family planning services, together with health and nutrition education for the mothers. The child-feeding centre provides clinical treatment and nutritional rehabilitation to malnourished children who are referred from the MCH clinic, together with practical instruction to mothers on child health and nutrition.

Services provided by the MCH clinic and the child-feeding centre have always been, and still are, heavily in demand due to the inadequate government services in the city, and because of their reputation for high quality service. However, shortly after the reorganisation of the whole programme in 1978, a major policy review was undertaken after local staff had identified the following problems:

– Many of the poorest slum dwellers seldom attended either the MCH clinic or the child-feeding centre. Staff felt that this was mainly due to socio-economic reasons. Furthermore, of those slum dwellers who did attend, the drop-out rate before recovery was extremely high.

– Follow-up of early drop-outs was extremely difficult due to the large catchment area and high mobility of the slum population.

– Many children who were brought to the clinic were often seriously ill and malnourished, making medical management and preventative education difficult.

These case studies emphasise the constant need for flexibility and reorientation. In response to the problems faced by URBAID, an attempt was made in 1980 to train a group of seven women,from one of the major slum areas in the

86

city, in motivational techniques and basic child health measures. The training course lasted four months and the aim of the project was for the women to pass on their basic practical skills to their neighbours,and to refer sick children to the MCH clinic for treatment at an early stage. This new venture failed to take off, however, apparently due to the non-cooperation of the slum families. What they wanted was not education in child health measures, but basic medical facilities in their own locality. They wanted improvements in their deplorable sanitary facilities and clean water; and they wanted a means whereby they could improve their income so that they could buy enough food for their families. URBAID did not proceed any further at the time, but the experience laid the foundations for future developments. Setbacks such as these have to be regarded as an unfortunate but essential part of the learning process.

It was in 1983 that URBAID finally decided to take up one of the demands of the slum residents which they felt was within their own capabilities and experience. They would take their health services to the doorsteps of the slum dwellers. Local staff felt that "....a slum community programme which worked with a defined population on a regular basis would not only enable easier access to those in need, but would also enable early detection of malnutrition and make preventative health work more effective," (from an URBAID report). It was proposed that they choose a slum area which was particularly badly neglected in terms of health services, and had also been in existence for a long time. Furthermore, it was proposed that a child-feeding centre and a new MCH clinic should be set up in the vicinity of the selected area to service the project.

**Selection of a slum community: what's in a land title?**

Initially, a poor and apparently stable illegal squatter settlement which had been in existence for over 30 years was chosen as a suitable project site. Approximately 700 families lived in the settlement. Permission from the appropriate authorities (who were the legal owners of the land) was secured to go ahead with the planned programme, and the long-term security of the residents was tacitly confirmed. However, two months after the initial registration of the slum families, the slum occupants were forcibly evicted under police pressure, illustrating the insecurity that illegal squatters constantly face.

This incident, together with a similar experience which happened concurrently to another non-governmental organisation (NGO) – People First (pseudonym) – who were working in another slum in the same vicinity, considerably influenced not only the criteria for selection of a suitable slum, but also the scope of any planned intervention. People First suffered considerable financial losses from the eviction as they had invested in upgrading the sanitation and water facilities and building a community clinic. These incidents clearly indicated to the URBAID project leaders that working in illegal settlements was risky enough; but it was more risky still to invest in physical infrastructure when the land did not belong to those who were intended to benefit.

After this incident, the project leaders decided to work in a legal slum. Medja Para slum (pseudonym) was finally chosen on the advice of the chairman of the Department of Urban Co-operation of the Municipal Council (DUC). The chairman, who was also responsible for co-ordinating government and NGO social services within the city, was already providing limited financial support – under the DUC's social services programme – to a boys' youth club in the slum to run a school for slum children. The youth club had apparently also requested the municipality to run vaccination campaigns in the slum. Recognising the initiatives of the youth club, but also their limitations, the chairman advised URBAID to move into this slum and assured them of the support of the youth club in their activities.

Successful meetings were held with slum community leaders, landlords and representatives of the slum tenants in Medja Para, and all parties concerned were eager for URBAID to begin their programme; and the youth club, as the chairman of the DUC had anticipated, promised all forms of practical support. But before looking any further at the URBAID slum programme – its progress and problems – mention should be made of the different groups within the slum, as these are the people who make the project, contribute to its orientation and condition its success or failure.

Penny Tweedie

**Degraded environments greatly increase the likelihood of diseases that heighten the prospects of malnutrition. Here in a slum in Kalipur there is intense overcrowding, pathways are undrained, sewerage is non-existent, and garbage is uncollected.**

88

## The Beneficiaries

### Who are the slum dwellers in Medja Para?

Medja Para is situated right in the centre of Kalipur city. The area contains a large slum population (estimated at 3–4,000 households), the majority of whom are 'legal slum tenants'. Within this locality URBAID identified a catchment area for its slum community health programme, which contained approximately 400 households (population around 2,000). The catchment area is geographically defined by a circular road network. The side and back streets are a hive of activity of the 'informal sector'. Scrap-iron and metal-crockery shops, which are located here, provide an important source of employment in the slum, and the site is within half-a-mile of the main trading zone, which is also a major employer.

Medja Para slum is well established, having been in existence for over 40 years. Environmental conditions are in general abhorrent, being over-crowded and insanitary. Slum housing, in which the tenants but not the landlords or youth club members live, consists of long rows of one-roomed shacks made of thatch/bamboo/scrap – known as *katcha* housing – many of which are in a bad state of repair, while the majority of the landlords and youth club members live in *pucca* (cement) housing.

There is no drainage or waste-disposal system. *Katcha* latrines and urinals, provided by the landlords, are poorly maintained and badly located near to housing or on the top of or beside the numerous ponds in the slum, which are used for bathing and washing clothes. Women queue for hours at the few roadside municipal taps to collect drinking water. The whole environmental situation is exacerbated during the monsoon months when flooding and overflow of the ponds and latrines create intolerable conditions for the tenants. Environmental diseases such as respiratory illnesses, diarrhoea and skin infections thrive in these conditions, often with fatal results for children; indeed, respiratory and diarrhoeal diseases were found to be the leading killers of children under 5 in the slum. Furthermore, URBAID surveys in 1984 and again in 1985 indicate that 67% of all children under 5 in Medja Para were either second or third degree malnourished, using weight-for-age as an indicator.

The majority (85%) of the slum residents are Muslim and are first generation city dwellers, having migrated from the surrounding rural areas because of economic hardship. Most have lived in Kalipur city for considerable periods of time (on average 22 years); but about 20% are fairly recent rural-urban migrants. Medja Para is fairly stable in its occupancy. The average length of stay is about nine years, although there is a constant flow of migration in and out, indicated by the fact that 29% of the households have resided in the slum for less than three years.

The population in Medja Para is predominantly a young one: 35% are under

10 years old, whilst only 3% are over 60. About half the households are nuclear, a third are extended families and only 10% are headed by women – the latter tend to be amongst the poorest – and the average household size is about 5.5.

## What are their sources of income?

The vast majority of slum tenants are totally dependent upon the urban market for both employment and food, and the slum economy in Medja Para is characterised by diversity rather than homogeneity. In a sample survey of 221 households in 1984, over 100 different occupations were recorded; and, as already indicated in earlier sections of this booklet, the majority of these earners are usually forced to eke out a living on a day-to-day basis, seeking casual employment as and when it is available. Normally only a small minority of earners are fortunate enough to secure permanent 'formal sector' employment, or possess their own tools and have enough capital to set themselves up as self-employed traders or skilled craftsmen. **Unstable jobs and low incomes place whole households at risk of malnutrition.**

In the 1984 sample survey only 2% of all household earners held permanent secure employment in the formal sector as peons, nightguards and industrial labourers, and were entitled to sickness and gratuity benefits, etc. 24% were self-employed traders – an extremely varied group both in the commodities traded and the size of the enterprise (for example, the financial value of capital in this group ranged from US$1 to US$3,100). 73% of household heads were casual workers. Of these, 56% were short-term wage-workers – rickshaw-pullers, daily labourers, cart-pullers, etc.; 8% worked on a piece-rate basis as tailors, matchbox-makers, paper-bag-makers; 6% had a regular income from working in small-scale unregistered establishments such as shops and small industrial units, but these regular wage-earners were not entitled to any of the statutory benefits. Finally, 28% were dependent hawkers who were solely reliant upon one particular larger trader for the supply of credit and/or goods. Examples in Medja Para included many of the scrap-iron hawkers, broken glass and plastic hawkers, metal-crockery hawkers and black-market sari-sellers.

When these households were classified by monthly income, the poorest 25% consisted almost entirely of casual labourers, whereas the richest 25% were almost entirely self-employed traders. The survey also found that there was a wide range in relative poverty in the slum. The average total monthly income of the richest 25% was eight times higher than that of the poorest 25%, even after taking household size and composition into account. Ownership of productive assets such as land, tools and business capital were almost solely confined to the richest 25% of slum households. An initial impression that outsiders may have that the slum is homogeneously poor is thus a fallacy: the distribution of resources even in urban slums is highly uneven, as it is in rural areas in the locality.

Women in the poorest households have to work (often for meagre earnings) to feed their children, but this gives them less time for child-care. Slum children with working mothers have sometimes been found to be the most malnourished. This woman in Kalipur earns US 10 cents (with which she could buy less than one third of a kilo of rice) for every thousand matchboxes she makes to help feed her child.

## What are their claims on food?

The inadequacy of income in the poorest 25% is indicated by the fact that 64% of households in this group were indebted – on average to a level three times their monthly income – to cover the costs of food alone; whereas none in the richest 25% were forced to take such consumption loans. Ironically, 40% of households in the richest group had access to subsidised food through the food ration system, compared with only 6% in the poorest group. All households in the richest group who possessed a ration card enjoyed the benefits of subsidised food prices, but none of the few households in the poorest group were able to do so: either they had mortgaged their ration card as security for a consumption loan, or they were unable to benefit because food obtained through the ration system had to be bought weekly, whereas the household earners were paid on a daily basis. The poorest households ended up paying more for their food even on the open market, as they were forced to buy it in small quantities in local shops where prices were higher than in central markets; and those households who took credit from these local retailers paid even higher prices.

One result of such intense poverty in the poorest households was the necessity to send as many able-bodied household members out to work as possible. 25% of all household members who were working at the time of the 1984 survey were female, and 10% were children under 15 years old. As might be expected, women and child labourers were almost solely concentrated amongst the poorest households.

The labour force in this region is highly segregated by sex. In the slum economy, work for women consists primarily of paid domestic work or home-based piece-rate work, both of which involve long hours and extremely low wages, both in absolute terms and in relation to male wages. As noted in earlier sections of this booklet, the children of poor households in which women work face increased risk of becoming malnourished because their parents are unable to afford safe and adequate child-care and appropriate feeding in the mother's absence.

Not long after the sample survey was completed, **a series was compiled of in-depth family profiles of households with the most malnourished children in the slum; these provide an understanding of the factors precipitating the nutritional crisis in such households. The profiles indicate that in these households it is not only the children who are severely malnourished, but also the parents – especially mothers – and siblings, indicating a total nutritional crisis at the level of the whole household.** These households came from the poorest stratum within the slum. Furthermore, adults were chronically ill with TB or asthma, etc. and mothers and older children worked in an attempt to buy food and pay the rent, the fuel bills and the interest on escalating debts. The children, who (URBAID records indicate) were severely malnourished and frequently ill from birth, were inevitably neglected in every sense in this fight for survival, being 'cared for' in their mothers' absence by their equally malnourished older siblings.

## The mediators in nutrition interventions: the local political economy

Clearly, the health and nutrition of the mothers and children in the slum are powerfully determined by the state of the physical environment and the terms and opportunities of employment. These are largely controlled by the influential political groups within the city; therefore any programme of health intervention that is comprehensive enough to take account of the factors relating to the environment and poverty must also take account of the local influential groups.

Even if health and nutrition interventions are precisely targeted, and formulated in terms of medical service provision alone (ignoring the social and environmental factors), experience has shown that the community's influential groups will still react to and concern themselves with the process of such interventions: for they will regard the administration of any programme as being, to some extent, subject to their control or permission. No project can exist in a political vacuum. We must therefore consider the main types of influential groups active in the case of Medja Para. They are: firstly, a group of exploitative 'employer-traders'; secondly, the slum property landlords; and thirdly, the youth club leaders.

### How is labour organised? Do slum 'labour lords' exist in Medja Para?

Unlike Chimbote, labour is not highly concentrated in one or two industries: the slum labour market in Medja Para is very diverse. There are industrial labour unions in Kalipur – but very few of the slum residents in Medja Para are industrial labourers. There are also rickshaw-pullers' unions fighting for better pay and working conditions for their members. But in general, labour in Medja Para is unorganised.

Unfortunately there are sad and extreme examples of exploitation of labourers through complex dependency relationships created by their employers (similar to those mentioned in the first half of this book); some of the dependent scrap-metal hawkers in particular provide an outstanding example of how people can be exploited and controlled with little hope of escaping and improving their own lot. First let us have a look at how these hawkers operate, and then unravel the various ways in which they are bonded to and exploited by their employer-traders.

Some of the scrap-iron employer-traders are established and powerful in the locality, and some are also slum landlords. Their shops are located on the back streets surrounding the slum. The dependent hawkers (who mainly live in one area of Medja Para on land owned by a landlord who is also a scrap-iron employer-trader) receive from their trader daily credit with which they buy scrap goods from homes, offices, manufacturing units, etc., in the city. The hawkers make their own assessment of the value of the goods and pay the seller according to the quality of the scrap and by weight.

At the end of the day the hawkers take the goods to the traders who, in turn, also pay the hawkers on the basis of quality and weight. Now the trader's

93

assessment and the hawker's assessment of the value of the goods often differ – leaving the hawkers out-of-pocket once they have repaid the daily credit. In such circumstances the traders are only too willing to extend consumption loans to their hawkers so that they can at least buy some food for their families. But the consumption loans have a hefty price. Exorbitant interest rates are charged – not overtly, but in the form of a daily commission on the prices of the goods traded – meaning that the hawkers get even less money. This leads to an increased need for the dependent hawker to take out further loans for consumption from his trader, and effectively bonds him to the trader.

Once the hawkers are bonded in this way, some of the employer-traders further gain from forcing them to work in gangs in shady 'wheelings and dealings' and in organised theft, out of which the traders make large profits.

Some employer-traders who are also slum landlords provide rooms in the slum and encourage nightly gambling sessions, which are attended by several of the parties involved in the shady dealings – including the scrap-iron hawkers; at least 10% of the night's gambling winnings goes as 'protection money' to these landlords/employer-traders, making yet another avenue for profit. These landlord-traders also provide loans to the hawkers for gambling, once again at high interest rates. Meanwhile the wives of the dependent scrap-iron hawkers feel devastated as they helplessly watch their husbands – who themselves feel frustrated at the lack of control they have over their own lives and destinies – gamble and drink away large proportions of their already meagre daily earnings.

In such circumstances it could be predicted that there would be opposition from these employer-landlords if any attempt were made to improve the supply of food at the household level through income-generating schemes. Such a venture may well be seen by these large traders as a threat to business. Alternatively such dependent workers may be unable to participate because of the scale of their indebtedness to the traders and consequently the level of control the traders have over them.

### Who owns the slum land and property in Medja Para and who are the community leaders?

Ownership of the slum land and property in Medja Para is currently claimed by 18 landlords, although disputes over boundaries and land titles are common and give rise to intense conflict between the families of landlords. 13 of them are original inhabitants of Medja Para and are related. The remaining five landlords have bought their land from some of the original inhabitants within the last ten years. Two of these recent landlords are property speculators who, in addition to renting out slum housing, are in the process of building multi-storey concrete apartment blocks – for rental by a different class of tenant altogether.

The land in Medja Para is unequally divided between the slum property landlords, and the economic status of the landlord families is not uniform: there are relatively well-off and relatively poor landlords, the latter being not

94

much better-off than their tenants. But most are self-employed traders with various scales of operation, and/or farmers.

The most influential landlord family is also, not surprisingly, the largest property owner in Medja Para. This large and extended family also owns several businesses and runs a large farm on the outskirts of Kalipur city. The family are original inhabitants in Medja Para, and have a history of leadership in the locality which stretches back over generations.

Associated with this family is what has come to be the most important social and political institution in Medja Para: the youth club. Many years ago the family founded a youth club in memory of one of their brothers who died during a period of civil strife. The club was originally a social meeting point for the local youth elite and this is still one of its major functions.

However, since its foundation it has become extremely influential in the locality mainly because of its involvement in local and party politics, and its increasing role in community representation and in negotiation with outside parties. Prominent youth club members now find themselves in the role of arbitrators in disputes within the slum; they occasionally provide loans to tenants and undertake 'welfare visiting'; they act as negotiators 'on behalf of the tenants' with outside agencies such as the police and other legal authorities (when tenants get into trouble), with the Health Department of the Municipal Council (to run vaccination campaigns for the slum children), with the DUC of the Municipal Council (in running a school for slum children), with local rotary clubs (for the distribution of free gifts to the poor), and with URBAID (in the initiation of their health project); and so on.

In the late 1970s the club registered with the DUC along with other youth clubs in the Kalipur district. This entitled them to a small annual grant to run a school for slum children, which they did on a voluntary basis.

At present the club has about 150 members – many of whom are college students – and it is politically affiliated to whichever party is in power. The youth club is run by a committee of seven and financed by monthly subscriptions from members and donations from the local elite. The present club president has been in position since his marriage to the sister of the main landlord 10 years ago; he is a businessman of moderate wealth, whose status and income have reportedly grown with his position as club president. Other prominent posts within the club hierarchy are held by other members of the main landlord family.

The influential status which the club leaders have acquired effectively means that they are now the political leaders of the slum. It is clear to any observer who has been there long enough that the basis of their influence lies in their **comparative wealth**, their **kinship connections** with the landlords and with the local government commissioner (who also lives in the slum locality), the **patronage links** which they have cultivated with governmental and administrative bodies in Kalipur, and their **physical power** (i.e. physical intimidation by numbers).

95

**URBAID move into Medja Para: a cautious start**

With at least some knowledge of the complexity of slum life, and still feeling stung from their previous abortive attempts in the illegal squatter settlement, URBAID project staff decided to move slowly. **Guided by tradition and their previous experience, they decided to start with the areas in which they were most confident – treating and preventing child malnutrition on an individual basis.**

At the very start of the slum project in the early 1980s, the youth club donated their club house as a project base, and nominations for community health workers (CHWs) were requested from amongst the slum dwellers themselves. After interviewing all nominees, one female and one male CHW were recruited and trained in the basic principles of child health, nutrition and first aid. They subsequently received continuous on-the-job training and supervision.

Apart from the two CHWs, the URBAID slum project is staffed by a Lady Health Visitor (LHV). The project is organised around a twice-weekly clinic in the youth club house and a home-visiting surveillance system, whereby all slum families registered with the project are visited once a month, with more frequent visits being paid to those households with sick or malnourished children or an expectant mother. The LHV and CHWs are supervised medically by a doctor, who also attends complicated medical cases referred from the slum clinic; and administratively by the URBAID project manager, who oversees all administrative aspects of the URBAID programme in Kalipur.

From the beginning URBAID laid down some policy guidelines:

– only slum families registered with the project would be seen, so as to ensure a good and manageable follow-up system;

– priority would be given to women and children, although other household members would be seen if necessary;

– complicated medical cases would be referred to outside specialised units;

– a nominal fee would be charged for the use of the health services, although this was waived in the early days in Medja Para.

The main components of the slum project are as follows:

**Interventions aimed at the individual level**

**Growth monitoring and health and nutrition education**

In order to monitor children's growth, the CHWs weigh all infants under 1 year old monthly, and weigh and measure the height of children aged 1–5 years at three-monthly intervals. Any child found suffering from third degree malnutrition or complicated second degree malnutrition is then referred to the child-feeding centre for nutritional rehabilitation. The CHWs plot the children's weight on Road to Health Cards, and discussions with mothers about the significance of and reasons behind rising and falling growth-curves is one important focal point for health and nutrition education, which reinforces the more formal education carried out by the LHV.

The LHV runs health education courses for mothers, and also for children attending the youth club school in the slum. The mothers' health education courses – which primarily focus on child health and nutrition – run for a period of eight weeks, and about 10–12 mothers attend twice-a-week. The groups meet in the slum and topics for discussion include, for example, the importance of feeding colostrum (which is generally discarded in this region) to newborn infants. The response to this campaign has been highly successful: **nearly all mothers now feed colostrum to their infants whereas before the URBAID programme was in operation this practice was rare.** Again, in an attempt to halt the slow but steady rise in bottle-feeding, breast-feeding is heavily promoted. There are also discussions about weaning; about the effect of common diseases (such as diarrhoea, measles and respiratory diseases) on the nutritional status of children; about the importance of diet during illness; about the use of oral rehydration salts (ORS); and about the importance of attending the clinic early in the course of an illness before further complications arise: illnesses such as diarrhoea are so common in the slum that they are not considered a health risk until the child's condition has become critical.

Many of these aspects are theoretically within the capacity of the mother to influence and hence are amenable to change. Whereas, **other aspects of the course dealing with hygiene and the importance of a more varied diet are more difficult for the women to tackle, given the conditions of intense poverty and the appalling environment in which they live. Indeed, knowledge, attitude and practice surveys conducted before and after such courses clearly illustrated that there were large disparities between knowledge and practice.**

As part of the continuing process of training CHWs, and for the purpose of compiling more appropriate educational materials, the CHWs recently conducted a child-feeding survey and combined the results of this with the growth-monitoring records of children under 5. The results in Medja Para have clear educational messages and could potentially reinforce the educational programme:

- children who were given solids in addition to breast milk at five months grew better than those introduced to solids either earlier or later;

- bottle-fed infants grew less well than breast-fed infants, and did not catch up even by 24 months-of-age;

- low birth weight babies (of which there were 35% in Medja Para in 1986) consistently grew less well than babies of adequate birth weight.

**Control of infectious and diarrhoeal diseases**

The components of the URBAID programme aimed at the control of infectious and diarrhoeal diseases include **curative medical care** and prevention through **health education** and **immunisation** (currently 85% of all children

97

under 5 in Medja Para are immunised against polio, diphtheria, whooping cough, tetanus, tuberculosis and measles).

Utilisation rates of the URBAID slum clinic are high, with over 2,500 consultations a year. However, experience has shown that, despite the availability of a high quality free service, many mothers consult a range of health practitioners (including URBAID, drug stores, religious healers, homeopaths, etc.) in the search for the miraculous cure, without giving time for any one treatment regime to take effect. Furthermore, **there is a general opinion amongst slum dwellers that costly practitioners who prescribe the widest range of multi-coloured tablets and syrups at any one time (many of which are irrelevant to the disease) are clearly the best. Considering the direct impact of disease on the nutritional status of individuals, and the cost of medicines bought instead of increased food purchases, an educational campaign directed at the drug issue would be of great relevance to the slum dwellers.**

### Prevention of Vitamin A deficiency

Vitamin A deficiency is a major nutritional problem. A recent survey found that the situation for children of the urban poor in the region was worse than that of the rural poor : the estimated prevalence of active corneal lesions in children under 5 is 16.3 per 10,000 compared with 10.2 per 10,000 in rural areas. These figures are respectively 16 times and 10 times in excess of the WHO criteria for a problem of public health significance.

Deficiency of Vitamin A may be due to diet alone, but it is often precipitated by measles, diarrhoea and intestinal parasites. Children who are malnourished are at greater risk of suffering from Vitamin A deficiency diseases than those who are not.

The URBAID strategy for the control of Vitamin A deficiency diseases in Medja Para includes promotion of foods rich in Vitamin A (such as green vegetables, mangoes, papaya, and oil to aid absorption); distribution of high potency Vitamin A capsules to children from 6 months to 5 years old; and immunisation against measles. Indeed, international research has shown that immunisation against measles is the most important single primary health care intervention to reduce the prevalence of blinding malnutrition. Before the URBAID slum programme was in operation, several cases of severe Vitamin A deficiency were found in Medja Para. Since the commencement of the project, however, no new severe case of Vitamin A deficiency has been reported.

### Family planning services and ante-natal care for pregnant women

It has already been noted in earlier sections of this booklet that longer birth intervals can dramatically improve the health of slum children and their mothers. The URBAID family planning activities include motivation, counselling, provision of method of choice and follow-up services. Motivation and counselling cover all available methods of contraception, but only Depo-Provera (DP) injections and oral pill cycles are actually supplied by the project. Women interested in intra-uterine contraceptives or in sterilisation, for example, are referred to government clinics.

There has been some progress in the uptake of family planning services in Medja Para, despite difficulties encountered in, for example, motivation and in the maintenance of a regular supply of DP injections; and because women receiving DP injections reported side-effects. In 1984, 16.6% of active couples accepted family planning, whereas in 1986 this had risen to 30%.

Almost all women in the slum deliver their babies at home and are assisted by local midwives. The URBAID ante-natal programme has aimed at reducing maternal mortality and infant mortality due to tetanus, and at detecting complicated pregnancies for referral to the local maternity hospital. 14 local traditional midwives have been trained by URBAID, mainly in the importance of hygienic practices during delivery and in the use of midwifery packs (which are sold to mothers by URBAID at the time of delivery and contain sterile blades and gauze to cut and dress the umbilical cord after delivery). 91% of all mothers who delivered during 1985 used midwifery packs, and 88% of all women of child-bearing age have been protected by anti-tetanus vaccines.

In 1985/86, the infant mortality rate in the three URBAID-serviced slums (population approximately 4,000) was calculated to be 95 per 1000 live births, compared with the national average of 125 per 1000 live births. This level is still very high. The levels of child malnutrition are also high, and there has been little change between 1984 and 1986 in the proportion of children malnourished (in both 1984 and 1986, URBAID surveys found that about 67% of children under 5 suffered from second or third degree malnutrition, using weight-for-age as an indicator). The continuation of such high rates of infant mortality and malnutrition, despite an intensive health service, is likely to be the result of the continuance of extreme poverty and a detrimental environment.


**Community level interventions**

In addition to the individual level interventions by URBAID, the Municipal Council through the DUC has been working, almost since the inception of the URBAID slum project, to improve the sanitation facilities and the economic conditions of the households of the urban poor. The DUC has provided a number of latrines and tubewells in Medja Para, in addition to running an income-generating credit scheme for slum families to encourage their existing trades and skills. A large proportion of the families living in Medja Para have been covered by the credit scheme and the repayment rate is reported to be good.

## Relationships between the local influential groups and the intervention project

## Relationship between the youth club and the intervention project

The relationship between URBAID and the leaders of the youth club has been extremely tenuous and unstable, especially during the first three of the four years that the slum project has been in operation. This instability has obviously been a result of differences between the objectives of URBAID, which aims to reach the most vulnerable groups within the slum, and the objectives of the youth club, which are grounded in self-interest and self-advancement. For example, youth club leaders made every attempt (albeit unsuccessfully) to control the siting of donated tubewells within the slum so that they were beside their own premises rather than in a position convenient for the slum tenants – the intended beneficiaries. Further, right at the very beginning the club leaders were instrumental in the selection of CHWs: they had successfully pushed their candidates for selection by URBAID and, unknown to URBAID at the time, their candidates were club members. However, this move on the part of the youth club backfired because the CHWs, who were sincerely dedicated to their work, consequently rose in status amongst the slum dwellers and refused to be controlled by the club leaders. The club members perceived this as a threat to their own status, so the club leaders made false allegations against the CHWs and unsuccessfully pleaded for the termination of their service.

It was also clear that the youth club leaders had intended (and succeeded in) using the URBAID project in Medja Para to enhance their own prestige and authority in the locality and to promote their own local political careers. For example, they advertised URBAID services widely in the local cinemas and press, **under their own banner**.

URBAID local staff handled these situations as tactfully but as firmly as possible, for they realised that any friction or breakdown in relations between the youth club leaders and the project staff would lead to difficulties in the continuation of the project. Indeed, the URBAID approach during the early years was one of diplomacy. Local URBAID staff took time to explain to the club leaders the aims of the URBAID approach and to keep them informed of all decisions taken internally regarding the slum project. They felt that understanding and true collaboration between all interest groups within the slum must be one of their ultimate objectives, being essential to the long-term success of the project.

In Medja Para, however, tensions between the agencies and the youth club leaders really came to a head in 1984 when the Municipal Council, through the DUC, proposed to build a multi-storey health/social complex within the slum itself. This complex was to include a children's hospital, a crêche, a school and income-generating projects. In order to understand the nature of the problems it is necessary to appreciate the relationships between the agencies and the youth club leaders.

## The importance of inter-agency co-operation

The history of the relationship between URBAID and the Municipal Council's Department of Urban Co-operation goes back to the initial planning and setting-up of the slum community project. As URBAID is registered with the Government's Department of Urban Co-operation it was essential to have an agreement with a local representative on the Municipal Council in Kalipur before any initiatives relating to community projects could begin.

As mentioned earlier, the chairman of the DUC in Kalipur was not only supportive, but also co-operative in the selection of a suitable project site; and since the beginning, URBAID have kept the local Department informed of progress in Medja Para. This relationship has been further strengthened after the Department initiated its own project of environmental improvement and income-generation in Medja Para.

As both URBAID and the Kalipur DUC were working in Medja Para, it was felt that they should collaborate to avoid duplication. The DUC, in conjunction with the youth club, formed a committee within the slum to oversee their income-generating programme. This slum committee was attended by representatives of the DUC, URBAID, the youth club, the landlords and the slum tenants. Inter-agency relations at this time were excellent, aided by the fact that there was a consensus of opinion between URBAID and the DUC about policy in Medja Para: **they would supplement rather than duplicate each other's activities, and their approach to the youth club leaders would be uniform and along the diplomatic lines described previously.**

However, in the mid-1980s the basis of this understanding broke down with a change in the senior staffing of the DUC. The new chairman had an entirely different approach and advocated a capital-intensive programme in Medja Para. He strongly urged URBAID to invest in, for example, a large *pucca* (cement) clinic within the slum and to appoint a full-time doctor there. But URBAID declined, since this was outside the original inter-agency agreement, and was in conflict with their planned approach.

The 'independent' rather than 'co-operative' development which unfortunately followed led to periods of intense instability and tension within the slum, as a result of differences in aims between the agencies and the leaders of the youth club. The inter-agency slum committee was dismantled; and the total breakdown in communication which ensued was tragic, especially as the chairman of the DUC had in the meantime drawn up the proposal for installing the health/social complex mentioned earlier, which could have implicitly replaced URBAID services in Medja Para. To compound the problems, the prominent club leaders inevitably took sides, and their self-interest and the extent of their local influence and power became clearly evident.

One year later, however, the inter-agency committees had been reintroduced and inter-agency relations restored. The instability had to have a limited life of its own. In the event, the DUC's proposal for the health/social complex was turned down by higher authorities as inappropriate; also a new chairman of the DUC came in as a result of routine rotational policy.

### The Kalipur Department of Urban Co-operation and the employer-traders

Apart from giving a valuable insight into the problems of inter-agency co-operation and the role of local powerful groups, **there is one particular aspect of the Kalipur DUC's programme in Medja Para which is worth documenting, and that relates to the success of the income-generating scheme in decreasing the heavy dependence of the scrap-iron hawkers on their exploitative employer-traders.**

Surprisingly, the credit programme has not provoked strong resistance from the employer-traders, nor has it resulted in the non-participation of the dependent hawkers in the programme (but this may be because the pool of potential labour in the vicinity is very large). Indeed, many of the hawkers who were heavily indebted to their employer-traders, and who had received loans from the DUC, were able to and did repay their traders and thus rid themselves of their heavy dependence.

Many of them left the trade altogether, and some started a labour group with an enlightened leader. This group ran a type of insurance scheme for its members, organised so that the day's earnings of the group as a whole were divided by one more than the number of members working on that day; the extra wage was saved and used to pay members during periods of illness, as well as being shared between all members at times of religious festivals, for example.

### Relationships between landlords and the intervention project

The relationships between URBAID and the landlords in Medja Para have never been as fraught with problems and tension as with the youth club leaders. Indeed, relationships in general have been good and, despite one or two problems (e.g. the landlord who is involved in gambling refused the agencies access to his land for a time; as did another small landlord who feared that the agencies had an ulterior motive to confiscate his land), they have not interfered in the day-to-day management of the project.

URBAID's main concern regarding the landlords is that they are factionally divided because of land disputes, and hence are difficult to negotiate with on land matters; and that their primary motive is profit. Hence they display no interest in investing in environmental and sanitary improvements. Perhaps, considering the cost of upgrading, expectations that the landlords would bear the full cost alone were unrealistic. A few landlords have requested URBAID to invest in such a programme; but,whilst acknowledging the importance of the environment both from a health and a humanitarian point of view, URBAID feel that there is too great a risk of the target population being displaced (due to increased rent as a result of the upgrading), or evicted and replaced by a different class of tenant altogether.

102

**New directions**

Until recently the main thrust of the URBAID project in Kalipur was health service delivery. Indeed, although the local political and inter-agency problems clearly hampered new initiatives, URBAID staff would still strongly support and justify such an approach. For they believe that community participation initiated too early in the evolution of such a project could well lead to misunderstandings between the slum tenants (who are too used to election promises and want action) and the agency itself. **"Time must be taken to produce some good results for the people ........ and when they see the benefit it (the project) brings for them, they may well be interested to participate in money, kind or labour.** *But this is only one aspect of participation.* **If we want them to participate in controlling the factors determining their health, they should be provided with ..... necessary support to help them gain knowledge, skills, organisational capacities etc. to gain initiative,"** (from a report written by the project manager of URBAID in Kalipur). In fact this is the new direction which the project is beginning to take.

**Preparing the slum dwellers to participate – the Health Committee**

With improvements in the relationships between the different influential groups within the slum, URBAID proposed that a Health Committee be formed which would include representatives from the various interest groups. It was envisaged that this committee would slowly assume responsibility for the planning, implementation and management of their own health. The response was positive. The youth club nominated their president and secretary to the committee, and all the landlords were invited. Then URBAID staff suggested to the slum dwellers that they should choose their representatives carefully from amongst those who:

– were well-liked and respected by them,

– were able to move freely throughout the slum,

– were aware of slum health problems,

– were mature and friendly,

– had been living in the community for a long time,

– were literate.

As the URBAID programme focused on women and children, they also advised that more women were nominated than men. Although the tenants did select their own representatives, in practice they needed support and guidance from URBAID staff.

The committee meets at least once a month. Its main functions are to represent the slum dwellers' views on their health problems, to decide how these problems can be solved and to encourage active community participation in these processes.

The participation of the slum dwellers on the committee has been slow, as was

103

expected. But there has been some considerable progress, even in the short time that the committee has been underway. For example, a decision was taken by the committee that URBAID should charge a nominal fee to the slum tenants for the use of their health services, and that the Health Committee should be responsible for the allocation of this fund. To date, the money has mainly been used to pay for the costs of treatment for severely ill people who are referred to outside specialists. The committee also decided that the families of landlords and club members who were visiting the clinic for free medication should stop this practice, as it was primarily intended for the slum tenants; so now the elite families receive only vaccinations, consultations and prescriptions for their children.

Another success has been the development of a proposal for a children's education programme in the slum. This request came from the slum tenants themselves because the youth club school had been forced to close due to insufficient funding. A proposal has been prepared by URBAID local staff in collaboration with the Health Committee. If this new venture takes off as planned it will be a major stepping-stone, since all groups within Medja Para have agreed to contribute financially, according to their means, to the construction and running costs of the school. Up to this point, all project activities had been fully funded by URBAID.

A women's literacy group has been started at the request of the women themselves in another of the URBAID-serviced slums, and is running along lines similar to the children's education programme. Initially this was organised and funded primarily by URBAID, although there was a small contribution from the youth club and from the women themselves; but it took only a few months for the full operational costs of this venture to be fully met by the women and the youth club, with the URBAID input being merely advisory.

**Further training for Health Committee members**

With the growing role of the committee in stimulating community interest, the URBAID local staff have now made a proposal to the committee that selected women members be trained in various aspects of the work of the project, with a view to helping them to gain more knowledge and the confidence to take greater responsibility. URBAID staff have proposed that the women undergo a seven-week training course (four weeks in the classroom and three in the slum) on the practical aspects of mother-and-child health that are central to the project in Medja Para.

On completion of this training URBAID envisage that the women would work two-to-three hours a day as auxiliaries to the CHWs, in a motivational and support role. Importantly, they would not be URBAID employees, but would be accountable to the Health Committee and receive a small payment in recognition of their work, which would be met from the community contributions for drugs, etc. This proposal has been received with some excitement, and the new, active Health Committee could well be the springboard for tackling broader issues of local relevance in Kalipur relating to malnutrition, as such issues were tackled in Chimbote and Neiba Valley (see Sections 4.2 and 4.3).

## The Kalipur development forum

Another recent and important development which was initiated by the DUC, and to which other NGOs and government departments have given their full support, is the establishment of a forum for the exchange of ideas and information about urban development in Kalipur. The forum, which started in 1986 and meets every other month, is attended by almost all the governmental and NGO agencies working in the city and, to date, discussions have mainly focused on the project experiences of its members. A bulletin reflecting these discussions is published quarterly.

It is hoped that such active participation and exchange will promote understanding and collaboration between the various agencies in their efforts to improve the conditions of the urban poor. It is one of the hopes of URBAID that the forum can, for example, stimulate the Public Health Authorities (who have representatives on the forum) to provide water connections, waste disposal, latrines, etc., not only for Medja Para but for all the slum areas in Kalipur. **Such a forum has the potential to make a city-wide co-ordinated approach to the provision of services for the urban poor.**

# CHAPTER 5.


# CONCLUSIONS

This booklet is not intended to be a manual on how to conduct projects dealing with urban malnutrition. Rather we hope it will clarify and draw attention to the complex way in which the various aspects of urbanisation impinge upon the individual's nutritional status. If the causes of urban malnutrition are to be understood, there are many inter-relating factors which have to be taken into account, such as: the urban employment structure, the slum environment, community politics, government price policies, and the strategies of multinational corporations. These factors tend to be particularly concentrated in urban areas, partly because the national and international market economies tend to operate more intensely there, and partly because of the higher population density in such areas. The three case studies in this booklet are particularly good illustrations of this complexity and, in the course of each study, we have emphasised the implications for nutrition.

The case studies, however, do more than provide illustration. They show how intervention projects have attempted to come to terms with urban complexity in diverse and imaginative ways. The Neiba Valley project, for example, instituted socio-drama and poetry to bring home to the people the importance of some of these inter-relationships; it used the principle of Paulo Freire's educational method to encourage people to draw upon their own experiences of how social structure and nutrition relate to each other.

The Chimbote project instituted the taking of a community census by the people themselves, and the mounting of an exhibition, to help them appreciate the social and historical roots of their nutritional condition. Both these projects also involved their people in scientific surveys: not only did this help them to perceive, for example, the connection between water-quality and nutrition, but it also provided them with data which they could present to the local authority in support of their cause. Perhaps the best illustration of urban complexity at the community level is the Asian case study. Here, the project organisers were imaginative enough to come to terms with the local political forces with a flexibility that allowed them to continue and diversify their work, despite the constraints they faced.

In some cases projects have diversified, in response to an increased apprecia-tion of the complexity of factors affecting nutrition, by initiating interventions at different social levels. In the case of the Neiba Valley and Chimbote projects, what had (at an early stage) been mainly a nutrition recuperation or food supplementation programme focusing more directly on the individual, later became projects that focused more on the community by organising education programmes and attempting to promote environmental cleanliness. Some projects attempted interventions at the national level, as when the problem of obtaining fresh water supply was tackled.

It is possible to see these projects changing their focus in response to frustra-tion over the constraints they face in any particular intervention: for instance, clinic-based feeding of the individual child is of limited value if the house-hold's physical or financial condition cannot be improved; and promoting cleanliness within the house is of limited value if the slum environment is not improved. At the same time these projects have continued to diversify in the way they seek to improve the individual's nutritional status **directly**, as when the Neiba Valley project engaged the help of a local radio station for both social educational purposes, and to broadcast menus using local products.

Perhaps by showing the evolution of projects over time, the case studies also serve to illustrate a further point: that the outcome of nutrition intervention is not necessarily either predictable or measurable. The effects of such projects may go beyond an immediate measurable improvement in nutritional status. The initial project may, in fact, act as a catalyst for further developments that will eventually have an even greater effect on nutritional or general health improvement. This is probably especially so if the programme contains some elements of health education, to heighten the community's awareness of the broader context of nutritional issues.

These projects show the potential for diversification in various directions, in order to come to grips with the inter-relationships we have described, and to harness the forces they represent. The direction or approach these particular projects have taken cannot, of course, be exactly paralleled in other urban areas. Political and cultural constraints differ, and details of interventions have to be tailored to specific situations; that is one reason why we have not written a manual. But we should like to think that these studies may stimulate and inspire the initiation or development of similar projects, approaches, and responses to the complex problems we have described.

Ultimately, however, we are aware that major sustained progress in combat-ing malnutrition cannot be achieved unless there are fundamental changes in society. One theme that comes up again and again, and is particularly well-illustrated in the Asian case study, is that environmental hygiene, which is crucial for good health and nutrition, cannot be ensured as long as the ownership of urban property is concentrated in the hands of a few. Such control gives slum dwellers no security of tenure and therefore little incentive to campaign for the facilities necessary to improve their own environment. Indeed, if landlords do upgrade their slums, there is always the danger that the poorer tenants would be displaced and hence gain nothing in the process.

Another common thread, which was illustrated in the Chimbote case study, shows how sufficient income to buy food for the family can only be achieved if contractual employment is secure and reasonably paid and on equal terms for women and men; this will never be the case as long as workers can be laid off when trade falters, or as long as women are regarded as a cheap reserve labour force. Furthermore, children's health cannot be ensured as long as the working conditions of their parents are kept incompatible with child-care.

A third point – which was clearly brought out in the context of the Neiba Valley – is that malnutrition is unlikely to be permanently banished as long as the benefits of an export-orientated economy are unequally distributed among the producers, and as long as the disadvantages of being a trading nation in deficit (subject to the dictates of the IMF) are suffered disproportionately by the poor.

Finally, it should be emphasised that much of the population pressure in the cities could only be reduced if rural livelihoods were made viable and the increasing polarisation of ownership of rural assets were reduced.

These are all fundamental political questions concerning the allocation of power. They cannot be tackled directly by nutritional projects; but their underlying importance in the causation of malnutrition has to be understood and constantly borne in mind.

In conclusion, it should be stressed that urban malnutrition is not only a complex problem but also an urgent one: by the turn of the century one-half of the world's population will be urban, and a substantial proportion of that population in the Third World will be living in slums. The speed with which this situation is being reached indicates the urgency needed in understanding the problem and the possible routes to appropriate interventions.

# OXFAM BOOKS ON HEALTH


## Selective Feeding Programmes
Practical Health Guide No.1

Oxfam Health Unit

A new version of the Oxfam Selective Feeding Procedures Manual originally produced to accompany Oxfam's emergency feeding kits for the Ethiopia Famine of 1973/5. This revision incorporates Oxfam's more recent experience of famine relief and now includes assessment and nutrition surveys.

*Also available in French.*

**Oxfam 1984. 92pp illus. ISBN 085598 097 4**


## Practical Guide to Refugee Health Care
Practical Health Guide No.2

Oxfam Health Unit

Based on many years' experience of refugee programmes, this revised edition provides criteria for assessing refugee health needs, enabling relief workers to gauge the appropriate levels of response. It contains appendices on all the important elements of an emergency health care programme.

*Also available in French and Spanish.*

**Oxfam 1986. 47pp. ISBN 085598 098 2**


## Implementing Multiple Drug Therapy for Leprosy
Practical Health Guide No.3

Dr. A. Colin McDougall

The system of multiple drug therapy for leprosy recommended by the World Health Organisation in 1982 is an extremely effective treatment which, if widely introduced and effectively operated, could result in a dramatic reduction of the incidence and severity of leprosy throughout the world. This book deals with a variety of aspects of the care and management of patients undergoing multiple drug therapy.

**Oxfam 1988. 43pp.   ISBN 085598 092 3**

## Tuberculosis Control Programmes in Developing Countries
Practical Health Guide No.4

Dr. Paul Shears

This manual aims to assist health workers and project leaders at village level to implement effective TB control in conjunction with national control programmes. Using research from various sources, it attempts to combine the most recent developments in the scientific understanding of TB with the realities of working at primary health centre level.

**Oxfam 1985, Revised 1988. 64pp. ISBN 085598 096 6**

## Controlling Iodine Deficiency Disorders in Developing Countries
Practical Health Guide No.5

Dr. David Phillips

Endemic goitre, cretinism and other iodine deficiency disorders can be prevented by the administration of iodine. This book gives advice and guidance on the organisation of iodine supplementation programmes. It deals with carrying out goitre surveys, recording the data, assessing the results, implementing a programme and monitoring and evaluating its success.

**Oxfam 1989. 32pp. ISBN 085598 107 5**

## Registration in Emergencies
Practical Health Guide No.6

John Mitchell and Hugo Slim

Based on Oxfam's wide experience of administering relief operations in a variety of emergency situations, this manual gives a step-by-step guide to assessing the need for and setting up a registration system. The lay-out of the registration site, selection and training of staff, organisation of the registration process, design of ration cards and the recording of information are all covered in detail.

**Oxfam 1990. 54pp. ISBN 085598 128 8**

## Health and Revolution: the Nicaraguan Experience
Richard Garfield and Glen Williams

This book looks back over ten years and records the development of health services in Nicaragua. A fascinating and comprehensive account of one country's struggle to provide appropriate health care for all its people in the face of enormous difficulties, *Health and Revolution* deals honestly and objectively with the failures and successes, and provides many useful lessons for other developing countries.

**Oxfam 1989. 242pp. ISBN 085598 131 8 Hardback**
**085598 132 6 Paperback**